Person to Person

Establishing contact and communication with
people with profound learning disabilities
and extra special needs

Person to Person

Establishing contact and communication with
people with profound learning disabilities
and extra special needs

Phoebe Caldwell
with
Pene Stevens

Pavilion

Person to Person

Phoebe Caldwell
with Pene Stevens

Published by:
Pavilion
The Ironworks
Cheapside
Brighton
East Sussex BN1 4GD
Telephone: 01273 623222
Fax: 01273 625526
Email: info@pavpub.com
Web: www.pavpub.com

First published 1998. Reprinted 1999, 2001, 2002.

ISBN 1 900600 43 9

Pavilion is committed to providing high-quality, good-value training materials and conferences, and bringing new ideas to all those involved in health and social care. Founded by health and social care professionals, Pavilion has maintained its strong links with key agencies in the field, giving us a unique opportunity to help people develop the skills they need through our publications, conferences and training.

Editor: Anna McGrail
Page design and typesetting: Stanford Douglas
Cover design: Métier Design Consultancy
Printed by: Intype (London)

The greatest obstacle to conversation
is not knowing the heart of the person
one speaks to…only when people
learn to speak to each other will they
begin to be equal.

Han Fei Tzu
3rd Century BC

Acknowledgements

Thanks to all the people I have worked
with and all the people I have learned from,
without whom this book would not have
been possible. Thanks also to Jane Routh for
her practical help and Anna McGrail for her
editing.

Phoebe Caldwell

Contents

FOREWORD

For over 20 years Phoebe Caldwell has shared her ideas, experience, and enthusiasm with carers and professionals. Her extraordinary career began when she found that she had time on her hands after her children had grown up. She had no professional training as a therapist and first encountered people with learning difficulties when she worked as an unqualified helper in the occupational therapy department of a long-stay hospital. She soon recognised that she would need to use a wide range of sensory modalities if she were to communicate effectively with her clients. Her new-found skills as a model designer proved handy. She manufactured special equipment and developed novel techniques to enable her to get closer to the severely disabled people with whom she worked.

When I first met her in the 1970s she was designing and building large-scale jigsaws and puzzles for individuals who had perhaps never had the opportunity to work in collaboration with another person. She learned quickly from her experience. Her awareness of what could be achieved through touch was soon augmented by experimentation with the use of other sensory modalities. She used sounds, vibrations, mirrors, and a variety of sensory surfaces to engage with those who found normal communication so difficult. She has developed her unique approach on the basis of careful observation and brilliant intuition. But in this manual she reminds us that techniques, however sophisticated, are not enough on their own. We must also respect and recognise the different worlds which people with severe disabilities may inhabit. Their worlds will often be full of irrational fear and anxiety. The work of Phoebe Caldwell provides a powerful model of how relatively simple methods can enable people with even the most severe disabilities to communicate their choices and enjoy more fulfilling lives.

Oliver Russell
Director, Norah Fry Research Centre

INTRODUCTION

For the past six years, I have been looking at innovative ways of getting in touch with those people with learning disabilities who seem to be locked into a world of their own. Broadly speaking, they fall into two groups: those with very severe disability and those whose behaviour we find challenging. Quite a number of the people whose behaviour challenges us will also have autistic features.

While it seems that, although they may overlap, these two groups have little in common with each other, our problem is the same: how can we find ways of getting in touch with people who are not able to respond to current service provision? They do not respond to our initiatives and we feel we are getting no feedback.

The work described in this book is not just about techniques but about the whole way we relate to people in all aspects of their lives. It is about the different worlds that each one of us carries and how, if we truly want to get to know each other, we must recognise and respect actualities which are not the same as our own. We need to understand how other people's realities are for them.

While some of the work has been done with children, most of the histories described in this book are interventions with adults, the majority of whom have spent long periods in institutions. Many have only recently moved into community homes and the expectation that it is possible to communicate with them is relatively new. It was easy to overlook an individual who sat quietly and rocked in a large ward or to think in terms of containment of a person with challenging behaviour. However, in small group homes, we are face to face, our individual personalities more exposed. We have the opportunity and the need to be able to communicate with each other but in order to do this we have to take into account our different ways of sensing realities – I may not see things the way you do.

This is particularly true of people with autism and can be a major source of stress for them. Although autism is not necessarily linked with learning disability, a proportion of people with severe learning disabilities have autistic features. Much of what we are learning about autism is written by people who are high-functioning and the question arises as to whether or not this is applicable to people whose autism is compounded by other disabilities. My experience is that, making allowance for the possibility that what we now term 'autism' may turn out to be an umbrella term for a number of neurobiological disturbances and also for the complexity of their disabilities, in practical terms it has always been helpful to apply what we can learn from high-functioning people with autism as an indicator of the direction to take with those who are low-functioning. In this book, for all the people involved, I look at a combined approach which seeks to reduce stress at the same time as building confidence. As well as looking for a common language, I explore issues which may be contributing to withdrawal or disturbed behaviour so that we can then look at how to modify events and interactions which an individual finds painful. In order to meet their needs, we may need to adapt ourselves to their world.

This work combines my own approach (which involves finding out what an individual likes doing and discovering creative ways of using this to enlarge their experience, as first described in *Getting in Touch*[1]) with the work of Ephraim[2] and Nind & Hewett[3,4] which is now known as 'Intensive Interaction'. It also draws heavily on the creative insights provided by Williams[5] and others who are able to write about their autism.

The title of this book is *Person to Person* as I want to emphasise an approach which is about relationship. It aims to shift our attention away from the problems a person presents to the difficulties they experience. Bearing in mind that current service provision is unable to reach these people, this approach is predicated on a radical change in values. In order to get in touch, we must cease trying to bend their behaviours to our world and enter into their world, as they experience it. While being aware of the dangers of projection, I want to know, as far as possible, how they perceive their world – how it feels to them. Within the parameters of where they feel safe, how can we enlarge and enrich their experience? How can we increase their confidence and help them to 'feel good' about themselves and others?

The objective of the person-to-person approach is to help individuals to feel safe and interested enough to move from the solitary occupation of self-stimulation to shared activity, from the closed loop of talking to themselves to a situation where they can explore, negotiate and interact with the environment and people around them. Then we can learn from each other.

Some of the histories in this book will be familiar to those who have read *Getting in Touch*, which was written as the outcome of four years' work supported by the Joseph Rowntree Foundation. Where they are offered again, it is to look at them from a slightly different and amplified perspective, to support new work or for completeness. That work which is new centres on the way we can use people's 'language' to communicate with them, not only in their ordinary daily lives but also when they are becoming distressed. It also looks at how we can support them by reducing the stresses they experience in their environment. It concludes with an appendix on training by Pene Stevens, drawing from her experience as the manager of a group of community homes. It looks at ways of setting up and maintaining such training.

Chapter One

FIRST STEPS TO LEARNING

As infants, we begin to relate to others from a very early age. We initiate signals and activities which are confirmed by the parent figure so that we are free to explore further. According to Stern[6] in his book, *The Interpersonal World of the Infant*, we build outwards from 'core self' to 'core other'.

We do this by setting up what I want to call a 'negotiating arena' between core self and core other. I introduce this term because it is sometimes difficult to talk about that part of ourselves which is defined by where we feel psychologically safe enough to engage with the outside world. This is the border-land between core self (where we have established and integrated our experiences) and core other. Using core self as a platform, the negotiating arena is the site of that more ill-defined and sometimes impulsive part of ourselves which gathers enough confidence to risk tentative overtures to the world outside: the border-land where we grow or shrivel. It is the critical area where we are strengthened or eroded by the responses we receive from the outside world and it is easier to discuss the potential and variable parameters of this area if we can visualise it.

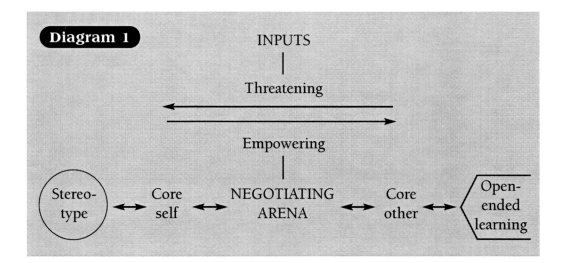

Diagram 1

INPUTS

Threatening

Empowering

Stereo-type ⟷ Core self ⟷ NEGOTIATING ARENA ⟷ Core other ⟷ Open-ended learning

When we are considering relationships, the negotiating arena is critical. I want to highlight it because it is here, within this arena, that all our external interventions, all the work we do, will be helpful and empowering or unhelpful and undermining. All our inputs will have to be weighed in the balance. We have to determine, not just whether we, through our realities, see them as proper working procedures but also whether the person with whom we are working can relate to them sufficiently in order to be able to accept them. We have to be flexible in the application of our models.

How does this idea of core self/negotiating arena/core other relate to the compulsive, repetitive behaviour that we call the stereotype?

Although it may overlap, the negotiating arena is not the same as 'personal space', which can be measured by physical proximity. It has more in common with feelings of self-confidence and security; its dimensions vary depending on the state of our lives and how this affects our ability to relate to the world outside.

Starting with infancy, if our lives are going well, we feel confident and open to risk, with new ideas, people and everything which is not self. In our expanding world, the arena feels safe enough for creative negotiation with 'core other'. We use language, whatever form it takes, to explore and exchange, confirming ourselves and others so that we and they grow in the world outside.

When our lives are going badly and we are afraid of what has happened, is happening or may happen, we erect protective barriers – we shut ourselves off from a world with which we cannot cope. The stereotype is at the extreme end of this continuum. Here the arena is completely shut down and the core self isolated. There is no potential contact with the world. Whatever language we have, we use it to talk to and confirm ourselves – nothing exists outside the boundary of core self.

Within and from the negotiating arena, we learn to adjust to the external world through a process which Stern[6] refers to as 'varied repetitiveness': each successive variation being partly familiar and partly new. The familiar guidelines render it a predictable place which can be controlled. Provided we can connect with them, it is a safe place in which we can graft in new but related concepts to our core self.

Ephraim[7] suggests that, for infants with severe learning disabilities, this process of adjustment appears to go wrong or never gets started. Perhaps because the infant is not ready, the parent/infant process is not synchronised. By the time the child is ready to participate, maybe years later, the parent has tried and become discouraged as there has been no response. The child makes noises or movements but the only feedback is those same sounds or feelings. What should have become an open-ended learning process becomes a closed loop of auto-stimulation which progressively excludes external stimuli as the person focuses more deeply on their own signals. They become stereotypically bonded on themselves; their repetitive world becomes their reality.

Stereotypic behaviour

Much of the work described in this book involves working through activities generated within stereotypic behaviour. The exact form taken by a person's stereotype seems to have a number of origins:

- **The core self is locked in on itself.** The repetitive behaviour has as its object part of the person's own sensory experience, for example, particular sounds and movements.

- **The core self 'hi-jacks' a particular object from the core other** as, for example, in people who are fixated on external objects such as doors and light-switches. Although these objects originate from the outer world, they are taken in and become part of the 'furnishings' of the core self. As above, the process of fixation excludes contact with the outside world. However, experience shows that both types of stereotypic behaviour can be used as access points to the core self.

- **The boundaries weaken:** the person's sense of the location of their core self becomes displaced. This is much more difficult and puzzling to understand but I have come across a few people in whom their whole sense of who and where they are seems to have shifted and comes from another part of their body. It is not just, for example, that they do not feel centred and that their interest is totally centred on, say, their knee. They seem to 'come from' there. Occasionally the boundary between core self and core other is so ill-defined that the person feels totally vulnerable to contact with other people and will avoid contact by running away. In such circumstances, it has been helpful to establish a physical boundary such as a screen (see page 41).

- **Pseudo-stereotypes:** there are some behaviours which appear to be stereotypic but have quite a different origin. Williams[8] describes how she spent two years flapping her hand to try to shake it off. It seemed to her to be an extraneous object with which she had no organic connection. The reason for this appeared to be that one of her ways of dealing with sensory overload was to switch off processing one of her senses, that is, she might switch off 'feeling' while retaining 'seeing' and vice versa. She calls this 'going into mono'. Because she could not see and feel simultaneously, the effect was to have no sense of her hand belonging to her. So she tried to get rid of it.

Because I believe that a person-to-person approach requires a fundamental alteration in perspective, I am now going to switch to the first person to give a sense of how profound our change needs to be.

Looking at the core self in its stereotypic form, from the inside it is:

- **Stimulating:** a conversation with myself confirms me in the way that my parent might have confirmed me. It lets me know I am here.

- **Closed down, safe inside:** my stereotypic behaviour is a fixed point, a beacon, in a confusing and jumbled world of sensory disinformation. I can refer to it and know it will be there. It is a non-threatening 'pseudo-other' which I can control. Contrasting the safety of his stereotypic behaviour with his chaotic sensory experience, Barron says: *'I know what happens when I switch the lights on and off.'*[9]

- **It excludes signals that are unfamiliar** and therefore potentially threatening: *'Objects are frightening. Moving objects are harder to cope with because you have to try and take in the sight, movement and further complexity of the noise. Human beings are the hardest of all to understand, they make demands on you which are just impossible to understand.'* Jolliffe et al.[10]

I have set up a very effective boundary to keep you out and you will have to find familiar and unthreatening signals which my brain recognises in order to reach me. You will need my Personal Code, which you can key in. When you have learned my language you will be part of my 'safe other' and we can talk to each other.

Chapter Two

FINDING THE WAY IN

How can we reach people who appear to be locked into their world, often absorbed in repetitive and stereotypic behaviours which exclude contact with the world outside their own?

One problem is that we frame our strategies on the basis of our own reality and not with respect to how the other person senses and perceives their world. We are also in danger of confusing communication with the ability to give or receive information. We want people to understand our requests; for example, so that they sit when we ask them to sit down.

Yet communication is about more than just getting someone to understand and respond to what is required of them. When we really communicate, we establish social contact and express sociability rather than specific meaning. By this type of phatic interaction, which may include language without words and more specific body language, we simply make it known that we are present for each other. We use gestures and small phrases to greet each other such as, 'Fine day today,' or, 'Doing all right?', which are not really about content, but rather to let the person know we are friendly. This type of communication is also known as 'strokes'. Perhaps one of the reasons why it is so powerful is that it may be a part of language derived from 'grooming' activities which conveys feeling rather than information.[11] I need to know that you are here for me. I need to give and receive intimate attention from 'core self' to 'core other'. By 'intimate', I am referring not so much to physical intimacy but to the total attention which embraces all that the other person is and does.

This is the most empowering way that we can get in touch with each other. It affirms and confirms us in our fundamental struggle to test our existence in the world as we experience it.

The following two histories illustrate the process of getting close to two people with whom alternative strategies have been unsuccessful. The first has very severe learning disabilities and the second, severe autism.

CHRIS sits all day curled up and scratches the arm of his chair with his forefinger. He does not look up or respond to stimuli.

I sit opposite him and scratch the far end of the arm, synchronising my scratches with his. It takes a while before he notices but when he does, he stops and listens. I do it again and gradually we are doing it for each other. We both begin to introduce small variations and take note of each other's. After a while, I introduce 'suspense' in the form of running my hand along the arm towards him and holding off before I scratch. Eventually, Chris puts out his hand, takes mine and holds it gently. He is smiling and looking up at me.

ROSE, a woman in her thirties with severe autistic features, lives in a community home. She sits all day and picks her head, pulling out bits of dandruff and examining them closely. She runs away if she is invited to participate in any activity.

I sit with the table between us and place some dried flecks of Tippex on the table. They resemble the flecks of dandruff which she finds so fascinating. She appears interested and looks at them carefully. When her attention is caught, I blow them gently so they move. She finds this funny and smiles. We move into a game of blowing them round the table. Since she has visual difficulties, this is helping her to track. We move on to blowing them with a whistling straw. She tries this, too, and laughs. We move through a variety of equipment, all of which incorporates flecks, ending with rolling a ball, covered with shiny flecks, to each other. The next time I come, Rose sees me coming and, instead of running away, she comes and leads me to the place where we worked before.

Both these histories illustrate the basic technique of Intensive Interaction, that is, we look and see what it is that the person is focusing on and feed back the same stimulus to catch their attention. In Rose's case, we are using interactive activities. With these, the signal that the person gives themselves is made more interesting by incorporating it into equipment or 'games' which are deliberately chosen to enhance the stimulus. This increases the element of novelty and hence, surprise. **Surprise is crucial**. Once we have found our way into the arena of exchange, it is surprise, presented in a familiar and therefore safe context, which extends both the potential of the interaction and the person's capacity to experience it.

Learning the language

In *Getting in Touch*, I used the analogy of entering a locked room. As I pointed out, this involves four stages:

1 Finding the right key

2 Opening the door

3 Exploring the treasures in the room

4 Looking out of the window.

I want to explore these in more detail here:

1 Finding the right key

In order to find the right key, it is essential to develop accurate and non-judgmental observation. We are often not as good at this as we think we are. We may only notice gross activities, such as position. For example, we may say that a person is 'sitting down' or 'lies on the floor' but this overlooks the particular activity on which they are focusing. We need to know *exactly* what is happening.

What is this person focusing on?

It is not always easy to spot activities such as digging nails into the palm of the hand inside a clenched fist, or to notice such sounds as the jaw clicking during chewing. Even if they are obvious, we have a tendency to 'filter out' those stimuli which are not significant to us. This is a trick we learn as children. It enables us to select, for example, the voice of someone we want to talk to in a crowded and noisy room. I am often told, 'No, he doesn't make any sounds,' of a person who is sitting still, gently grunting to himself. Even heavy breathing can be a source of self-stimulus, that is, the person focuses on this to the exclusion of external stimuli.

Furthermore, there are some stimuli which we reject on the grounds that they are socially unacceptable, for example, as in Rose's history above, picking dandruff out of the hair, or grinding teeth. Support staff will admit that they forgot to mention teeth-grinding as they did not like it, so 'switched off' to it. Besides, they could not see what potential it had for communication. **We must learn not to make value judgements based on our own reality**.

When we are making observations, it is important not to jump immediately to the obvious conclusions:

> **SARAH** clutches a folded crisp packet. I am told that she 'likes the noise'.
>
> A second look shows that what Sarah also likes very much is the 'feel', she is pulling at it regularly with her other hand. She very much enjoys it when I stimulate this area of her hand with vibration.

We need to draw up a list of questions to ask ourselves.

- Is this person making any sound at all, including such activities as heavy breathing or grinding teeth?

- Is this person making any movement in a repetitive way?

- Does this person like particular smells/tastes?

- If this person has any speech, is it focused on one subject? Are we really listening to what they are saying?

- Is there any object or activity (however passive the latter) to which this person is attached?

In order to find the right key, we need to detach ourselves from our own blueprints of what a person 'ought' or 'ought not' to be doing and learn to observe them as they are. What is it that is important for them? Can we find a way of using this to enter the negotiating arena so that we can talk to each other?

2   Opening the door

Once we have decided on an appropriate strategy to work with a person, using a language which we think they will recognise, we have to consider how to present such an approach in a way that will be acceptable, so that they will not only notice it and find it familiar, but also non-threatening. It is very important at this stage to be aware that the person with whom we are working may perceive the world differently from the way we do.

- The person may have physical disabilities which hinder reception of the signals we send them. For example, a person with tunnel vision will not see signs made outside their field of vision.

- The person may receive signals normally but be unable to process them, as happens with people with autism. For example, if we try to communicate verbally, the person may hear the sounds but be unable to attach meaning to them. This may happen intermittently (sometimes the processing works, sometimes not), which can mislead their support staff into believing that they are lazy or difficult. Such failure to process builds up pressure which is described as being 'overloaded'. Williams says:

'I keep running, running, running, trying to keep up.'[12]

- Overload causes 'fragmentation' – images and stimuli break up. This is a painful process. In my experience, it is sometimes accompanied by overheating – the person streams with sweat. (It is difficult for us to realise that it may well be our attempts to draw an individual into 'our' world which are themselves stressful and contributing to the difficulties they are experiencing. Again, Williams[12] talks about the tension and stress of always having to be in 'the world' and not in 'her world'.)

- For a number of reasons, some people reject our interventions. Perhaps the most obvious is that we are physically too close to them so that they are afraid. Another reason might be, if we put out our hand to touch an object they are flicking, they feel we are trying to take it away, something which has almost certainly happened in the past. (This can sometimes be overcome by using a duplicate so that we can join in without being seen as threatening.) It is also my experience that, where people have more than one repetitive behaviour, they may use one of them not so much as a conversation with themselves, but as a line of defence in order to keep out a world with which they cannot cope. At the same time, however, most people *are* carrying on some form of internal dialogue with themselves and it is this we need to be looking for.

- 'Normal' signals or even 'valuing' signals, such as a smile or eye-contact, may have a negative impact if the brain of the person who receives them understands them quite differently from the intention of the sender. (A person with autism may experience eye-contact or even direct speech as acutely painful.)

- The signal the person receives may be correctly processed but not connect up with familiar ideas. According to Stern:

'Each successive variation must be partly familiar, as well as partly new'.[6]

- There must be something recognisable in our signals for the person's brain to connect with. If we offer something which is totally new, we may be introducing expectations with which people cannot make connections. This sets people up for failure. This is particularly easy to do if we offer 'blanket occupations' – everyone is offered a particular activity regardless of whether they connect with it.

We therefore need to be aware that our well-intentioned inputs may be received as:

- indistinct

- intermittent

- confused

- distorted

- reduced

- unclear

- bottlenecked

- fragmented

- unmotivating

- disconnected

- positively threatening.

Intensive interaction

In the first two histories, we referred to the technique known as Intensive Interaction in which a person's behaviours are reflected back to them. This process is now well documented, especially in Nind and Hewett's excellent book, *Access to Communication*.[3] Further reflections on these techniques and their use with a wide range of people with disabilities are to be found in their more recent book, *Interaction in Action*.[4]

For the benefit of those who are not familiar with the method, I will briefly run through the way I approach the technique. I sometimes find, when I am teaching, that support staff only have a partial idea of how to go about it. They will speak of 'mimicking' behaviours and are 'not sure what to do next'.

- To begin with, the language we use is important since it determines the way that we think. Mimicry can have an undertow of mockery and uses the person as an object. There is a fundamental difference between mimicking and talking to a person in a language which speaks to their inner world in a way which they understand and with which they feel safe.

- Having decided what signals the person is giving themselves and focusing on, we start to reflect these signals back to them.

In principle this sounds simple, and it is – provided we are aware of various forms of interference which can arise.

- We may feel self-conscious – particularly when we are new to the techniques. This becomes less of a problem as we begin to get feedback and a sense of the essence of a person (rather than behaviours) in a way we have not experienced before.

- We may have been taught to work in certain ways which exclude a necessary flexibility of response. For example, we may feel that we have to 'teach' the person skills, rather than use activities as opportunities for sharing.

- We may have in mind ways of working with people with similar disabilities which have been helpful with other individuals. Such agendas can obscure the potential of the person with whom we are working – what they have to offer.

- We may doubt our ability and lack the confidence to be wholly present for the person with whom we are working, especially if we are not used to giving people undivided and what I call 'intimate' attention, something we rarely do.

- We may be trying to do too much at one time when the person needs to rest and assimilate what we are trying to do together. This is particularly true of some people with profound disabilities. Characteristically, they respond and then withdraw. We need to give people time to take in what we have been doing together. Birath[13] points out that, after a period of withdrawal, they will quite often sigh and then resume attention at the end of the 'assimilation time'.

- We may fail to trust the person with whom we are working. We need to empty ourselves and put ourselves in their hands – give them control.

Responses

When the person notices, they will usually stop what they are doing and look surprised. ('That's one of my signals but where did it come from?') You can see them attending.

Three points need to be mentioned here:

1 It may be some time before people notice the intervention, or at least they may notice but not respond. Even if they do, the responses may be very small, for example, a change in head movement or breathing rhythm. Using a stethoscope, Ephraim[7] even noted a change in heart-beat rate when he was working with a quadriplegic man.

Occasionally, it has been up to half an hour before I have noted a physical response, although I have kept going since I have had the 'feeling' that the person was attending – presumably through subliminal clues which were too small to identify. (I make it a rule to take note of intuitive 'feelings' and test them against practice.)

2 It is worth remembering that a 'stimulus' is sometimes the difference between the presence or absence of a signal, rather than the signal itself; for example, with vibration, the stimulus is the difference between the on/off rather than the continuous buzz.

3 Sometimes a person with hearing disability will signify their attention by turning their face away from the source of the intervention, rather than towards it. We are so dependent on eye-contact for confirmation that it is easy to mistake this for lack of interest, when it actually signifies turning their head to present their best ear. What is almost always clear is an alteration in the posture of the body towards 'alertness'.

Usually the person will wait to see if the unexpected signal happens again. After a pause, I will do it again. I will try to get us to take turns. They do it, I do it. At first I will mirror their actions, then, with touch, I may try joining in. I am trying to develop a conversation, using all the skills involved in this. Using their time-frame, I am alternating, listening and responding, giving space and adding new and related material. No two conversations are the same and I need to be totally focused on what the other person is showing me. I also need to show my pleasure in our meeting but always have respect for the way that they understand my signals. At this stage we are beginning to interact. One student said:

'It's like a jar of sweets. Each person has their own unique flavour.'

It is this flavour, this 'essence', that we need to look for and work with.

It is easy to make assumptions about people's capacities based on our interpretations of their responses or lack of them. We may suggest that a person is not motivated, when it is nearer to the truth to say they cannot connect with 'our world' but can be interested and innovative if we learn their language and enter 'their world'.

JOE, who will not normally initiate anything and seems to be completely without self-motivation, becomes interactive through using his rather complex inner language of card-sifting hand movements and sounds.

He becomes lively and experimental, introducing new movements and waiting to see if these are picked up. When they are, he is obviously pleased. He enjoys the exchanges. He is motivated and concentrates on what we are doing together for twenty minutes.

Testing the system

Having recognised the system, a person often moves on to test it. People may deliberately introduce new material to see if I am really listening and whether our new-found communication is reliable. I have been surprised by the sophistication of the techniques people have used on me to test whether they have control. The next two case histories illustrate this.

POLLY screams loudly about twice a minute. These screams seem unrelated to events, they just go on all the time. She cannot be taken outside and her behaviour affects all the residents and staff in her community home.

I try screaming with her. Every time Polly screams, I scream. When she first hears me, she looks very shocked and runs upstairs. I do not follow her because she has chosen to have that space and I must not encroach on her, but I can continue to echo her screams. She comes downstairs and looks at me round the door. Then she returns upstairs. I continue to echo her screams. After five minutes, she comes down and sits at the table with me. We move into exploring her noises, louder and softer. She puts out her hands and starts a series of hand movements which are not in her usual repertoire. It is as if, having been locked into her own world, she physically starts to explore the space outside her boundary. Her arena is enlarging. We do these movements together. She is smiling and relaxed.

Her key-workers undertake regular sessions with Polly, using whatever language she is using at that time. Her screams become less frequent and she is progressively more interested in hand contact and movements. By the end of six weeks, she has stopped screaming altogether. She can go out shopping with the others. Her quality of life has improved.

MARY, in her thirties, has total visual loss. She is difficult to work with as she hits and scratches. She appears to be unhappy. She has bits of string with which she plays. When she goes into a room, she walks round kicking the furniture and then lies down and drums her heels on the ground.

Mary's most obvious repetitive behaviour is playing with her bits of string. However, when I try to join in, she thinks I am going to take them away and so she scratches me. Next, I try drumming my feet on the ground. This immediately catches her attention. She stops drumming her feet and listens. I repeat my drumming. She repeats hers. We then alternate and she begins to smile. Next, she gets up and stamps round the room. I stamp after her. She lies down again. This time, I walk across the room slowly (stamping my feet to let her know where I am), lift my foot and step over her and walk to the far side of the room. By this time she is laughing out loud. She then gets up and introduces a game of 'Find you'. She knows where I am because I am stamping my feet. She comes up to me and gently nudges me and moves off laughing. She repeats this a number of times.

Kicking furniture is seen as 'problem behaviour' but actually Mary is doing it in order to know where she is in relation to objects, it is a coping strategy which she has developed to deal with her environment.

Continued...

The next time I visit, I stamp my feet to introduce myself but, to my surprise, Mary is very cross with me. I realise that, this time, she has taken her shoes off and is scraping her feet along the carpet. By stamping, I have conveyed the message that I am not listening to her, and the new way we have set up of talking to each other is not working. When I scrape my feet, she becomes calm and starts to smile again. Later on, she introduces tapping a tin as another way to communicate.

It is crucial that we remain open to any new material which is offered to us because not only does it convey that we are listening to and valuing the person and what they are doing, it also validates the new system. It confirms to the person that they *can* communicate and gives them confidence to try to extend the boundaries of the negotiating arena. ('I can use my language, the one I feel safe with, to talk to, negotiate with and affect "core other".')

It is no good using yesterday's material. We must respond to what the person is doing *now* – and our responses should never be mechanical. (This is why recording sounds and playing them back often does not work. Although the person may show initial interest, they usually lose this quite quickly. We need to be present and responding to what the person is offering at this time.) We should feel we are talking to friends, giving them time to reflect on what is happening and responding to their innovation.

Balancing familiarity and surprise

Problems can arise if no variety is introduced, either by us or by the person. We begin to feel that the process is no longer interactive, that we are being used and somehow we have become an object built into the closed loop of the person's stereotypic behaviour. Weighed in the balance of Stern's 'something familiar, something novel',[6] there is not enough new material to attract their attention to the outside world. They have become habituated. **Surprise has been lost and, in the model of the locked room, it is surprise which keeps the door open. It is the foot in the door which allows interaction to continue.**

Sometimes what is needed to make the shift is very simple.

MEG continuously drops objects in order to have them picked up. We return them to her as we feel she 'ought' to be holding them; we become part of her 'closed repetitive loop'.

How can we get out of this and use Meg's behaviour in a way that is both familiar, so that she accepts it, and new, so that it refocuses her attention outside herself? If we pick her object up clumsily, play 'butterfingers' and laugh at ourselves, we introduce surprise so that we can share a joke together.

If we take **sound** as the stimulus, we can look at it from the inside:

- I am surprised that my sound is coming, not from me but from 'out there'. I attend and look to see what is going on.

- Next, I notice that my sound is sometimes out there and sometimes not, it has become intermittent. The stimulus has shifted from just being an external source to the difference between 'there' and 'not there'.

- My sound is 'out there' but slightly different: part of it is familiar – enough for me to relate to – but part of it is new – what I recognise is linked to something I do not already know. This is the beginning of the learning process, the opening out and enlargement of the negotiating arena. I use what I recognise and feel safe with as a platform to explore new territory. On its own, it would be too threatening, but it is acceptable within a safe context.

In order to maintain both contact and surprise, there is a variety of options open to us when we work. If we take, for example, a person's **hand movements**:

- The person's movements can be **reflected back** in such a way that copies what they are doing. As has been pointed out, it may be difficult to get the person's attention by straight copying. Particularly where the stimulus is visual, they may be too locked into their inner world to notice.

- If we have the person's attention, we can strengthen it by **making the source discontinuous**. This not only provides stimulation but allows us time to reflect on what each other is saying.

- Where people are really locked in to a physical movement such as rocking, flapping their hands or hand-wringing, they may not notice if we mirror this. It may be more effective to **reflect the movement back in a different mode** – for example, through sound that mirrors the gesture, such as scraping a corrugated tube to the rhythm of rocking; or through touch – perhaps movement of a finger on the person's back or arm, or somewhere they find acceptable. We also need to think creatively. For example, we can enhance finger-flapping by designing a mirror with holes in it (as shown in the picture overleaf) through which 'their' movements can be made. This equipment not only encourages the individual to look at the stimulus that they enjoy but also draws their attention to their body image.*

- We can **physically join in** the movement, placing our fingers on theirs if they will allow us to do so. This is a process which requires great sensitivity and, if necessary, willingness to withdraw. Further, if touch is going to be used, then it needs to take

---

* Stern[6] throws light on why 'changing the mode' may be so effective. It is not only introducing variety but also empathetic. He says that if we copy a person, we let them know that we know what they are *doing*, but if we reflect back their actions but in a different way, through a changed mode, we let them know that we know what they are *feeling*.

place within the context of an
agreed management strategy
so that it can clearly be seen
to be non-invasive. There
is a difficult balance to be
drawn between privacy
and what may be the only
possible way to establish
the vital link between the
person's inner world and
the outside reality, between
isolation and participation.

Mirror with holes

- Even rejection itself can be
used as a way of interaction in that it allows the person to control the distance
between us. If I am pushed away, I can stay and work at that distance. By doing
this, I show that I am respecting the needs of the person with whom I am working –
she wants space and I am giving her control. Even if she does not want to work with
me at all, she may be intrigued by my respect for her; it will awaken her interest.

The following history illustrates the balance between habituation and surprise:

FRAN, a woman with autism, has two languages, one of which she uses on
her own when she thinks she is unobserved. It relates to her outer world: 'I'll go
on the red bus,' or ' ...in the green car'. Her other language clearly repeats what
has been said to her previously when she was being 'difficult': 'I'll get Sister!'

When she starts to walk round in circles and becomes agitated saying, 'I'll get Sister!',
it is possible to divert her by taking elements from her inner turmoil and switching
the context to her outer (if hidden) language, combining the two to draw her attention to the outside world. For example: 'You'll have to get Sister *in the red bus.*' Fran
is silent for a few minutes while she thinks about this.

This strategy works three or four times until she gets used to it and it no longer
stops her in her tracks. But switching to 'You'll have to get Sister *in her green car,*'
is surprising again, and again Fran is diverted while she thinks about it. Each time
there is a new element contained within the familiar response, something she is not
expecting, the surprise defuses her rising distress. Support staff are now using this
technique to help her when she is upset.

Adjusting to the individual

It is very difficult to lay down blanket guidelines. Each person is an individual with their own history. What works for one person does not necessarily work for another. We need to think more in terms of a jigsaw – as Williams puts it: 'which bits fit where' and 'how they are related'.[12]

> **RICHARD** is able to interact if his sounds are reflected back to him when he is happy, but when he switches to his distressed phases – something which happens very fast and may be related to epilepsy – trying to work with his sounds makes him increasingly agitated.

On the other hand:

> **ASH**, who is often very withdrawn, relates through touch with his many and diverse hand movements when he is distressed, but when he is 'happy' he prefers to relate through games such as 'thumbs up' and 'give me five' which are in the nature of party tricks. These, while being an expression of his happy state, leave no room for mutual exploration.
>
> For Ash, it may be more realistic and effective to work through his outer world, that is, his interest in boxing. For example, he enjoys looking at boxing magazines. (In the case of another person with similar interests, we used cut-out stand-up figures, as shown in the picture overleaf.)

A number of people with stereotypic behaviour have more than one repetitive pattern. They may move through a whole sequence and it is not always the most obvious signal to which they respond when we reflect back their behaviour. As pointed out above, some repetitive patterns may be defensive. Where there are multiple behaviours, we need to try all of them.

If the person with whom we are working shows any signs of distress or overload, we need to return to the original mode or way of presentation. We are working in an area where people have dropped their defences. We are inside their boundaries and they may be very vulnerable. It is crucial that we are aware of this and ready to withdraw at the least sign of unease. If the person becomes over-stimulated – as can happen occasionally, for example, with people with epilepsy or autism – we need to shorten the time of the intervention.

Boxing figures

We may be trying to work with people whose disabilities are extremely complex and whose lives are a hidden history of unhappiness. It is important for them, as well as for us, that we are not judgmental about ourselves if we are rejected, since there will inevitably be times when, even if everything went well last time and the intervention has been carefully thought through, the process does not work – the person with whom I am working does not want to know me. Although we had a marvellous 'conversation' yesterday, today the person gets up and moves my chair away. It is very important that I put my feelings aside and consider what actually happened. Did I get the timing wrong? Was I too close? Despite the fact that I used their language, did I get the presentation wrong? Do I need to introduce new material? Did I miss something or were they just telling me they have had enough?

3   Exploring the treasures in the room

We have found the right key, opened the door and are looking round to see what is in the room to share with each other.

The sharing has to be mutual. We have to be open ourselves and let people explore us. It is extremely important that we allow ourselves and our pleasure to be evident to them as this gives people the confidence to exchange. Using their language, we begin to introduce flexibility into the stereotype, opening out into an arena in which the core self can feel safe to negotiate with others.

> **SALLY**, a child aged five with severe autism, is completely locked into the idea of her family car. All she will say is, 'Mummy's blue car.'
>
> I make her a blue car, two sides with a box between. I am now able to place objects in the box and Sally is able to name them. They are literally contained within the familiarity of her stereotype which has been enlarged to admit new material.

> **DONNA**, a small girl, tears up paper and stuffs wedges of it in between her fingers. She is very upset if these are removed. It is extremely difficult to focus her attention on alternative activities.
>
> Her father does the same. Donna watches carefully. He takes his out and sorts them into piles. Twenty minutes later, she takes hers out and sorts them for the first time.

Both these histories show how, using the language of a person's stereotypic behaviour, we can begin to enlarge the negotiating arena, strengthening the area in which the person feels safe enough to interact. At this stage, we have not moved the person outside the stereotype in which their core self is anchored. Rather, the stereotype has become more flexible so that we are able to insert new ideas, new openings, which can be dealt with in the security of their familiar world.

Exploring the room is not only about discovering and increasing what the people with whom we work can do, but also about the more unquantifiable world of discovering who we *both* are. What can we learn about each other through our body language? How can we learn to trust one another and share each other's pleasure – a vital stage in making friends?

At this stage, support staff will often ask what they have to do next. This is a problem because we are conditioned to the idea that, in order to succeed, we must be moving on. There must be new goals in what appears to be a progressively upgraded obstacle race. The difficulty is that if we are locked into our own forecasts, we easily miss what the person with whom we are working has to offer. When this happens, when we miss their cues, it tells the person that their new way of relating to the world outside themselves is not effective. The outcome of this is loss of confidence and a return to their inner world. Williams[12] suggests that we put our own agenda in our back pocket. We need to keep ourselves in the present, trust the person with whom we are working, watching for their contributions and valuing them. This is the way to empowerment.

4 Looking out of the window

Inside this new flexible arena, which we enter by using the individual's 'personal code', and in which we communicate by using their 'language', whatever form it takes, the person:

- usually becomes more relaxed, not only during interventions but also spilling over into the time between. The person becomes more adventurous with us. At the same time, we need to be aware that the person may also be more vulnerable since we are working inside their defences

- will sometimes speak – from surprise, but within a position of safety
- can use the arena as a platform to view the world outside.

GEORGE, a young man with severe autism who attends a day centre, draws road plans repeatedly on an A4 pad. He is very upset if staff try to join in or offer alternatives.

Trying to share his drawings requires sitting very close to him. I decide to give him more space and place a very large sheet of paper on the table (one by one-and-a-half metres). This gives room for me to sit at one end with George at the other. We work towards each other, eventually meeting in the middle. He begins to enjoy my contribution and I am able to move into his side and he into mine. I add traffic lights and road cones to his roads and he starts to look outside, through the window, at those he can see in the road. All goes well until we introduce some model cars and try to drive them round his roads. This is too much and he becomes upset until we draw a car park and park them in it. We are able to contain George's normally disturbed behaviour during the lunch hour by continuing to focus his attention on our joint project. The following day his mother, who has been unaware of the intervention, phones the centre to enquire what has happened – she has never seen him so calm and relaxed.

George, in spite of his autism, enjoyed working co-operatively, provided he was given enough space to do so. When he did feel threatened by the cars, we did not have to take them away, but were able to neutralise his fear by enclosing them in a car park. We were using his 'language'. Because he felt safe, he started, quite literally, to look out of the window and compare and share his inner world with what he saw outside. His enjoyment of this sharing intervention overflowed into the rest of his day to the extent that his mother, who had not been present, noticed his changed behaviour.

The arena can be used as a launch pad to start exploring the world outside.

DANIEL is a young man who has recently left hospital to live with his family. He sits in a chair all day, looking at his fingers flapping. In spite of the best efforts of his family, he does not respond to their initiatives, except finger-flapping games or making animal shapes on the walls. The chair has to be tipped in order to prompt him to get up for meals, the toilet, and so on. He does like being pushed out in a wheelchair but in the winter this is not practicable as the family live down an unmade road which gets too muddy for this to be possible.

I am asked to see if I can find a way of interacting with Daniel so that, when winter comes, his family can work with him indoors. He responds to interacting with fingers; this is his language – the way he talks to himself. In order to widen his experience, I use a plastic mirror with holes (as shown in the picture on page 20). When he looks at my wriggling fingers pushed through the holes, an amplification of the stimulus he is giving himself, he also sees his face and starts to look at himself for the first time. I also design a box with holes in it (pictured below), through which a finger can be pushed. The aim of the game is to use a transparent plastic cup to catch the finger. So far, other than playing shadow games with him, it has not been possible to engage Daniel's attention. He needs hands-on prompt only eleven times before he is able to play by himself. He finds it very funny and enjoys the interaction. His family works with him daily. After about a month, Daniel stands up one day, picks up his chair and takes it out into the garden. This burst of self-confidence is the beginning of more normal interaction with his family. He goes where he wants to.

To summarise:

- When we are looking for ways of working with people who are locked into their own world, we need to observe each person's behaviours non-judgmentally in order to identify the language that they are using to talk to themselves.

- We have to find ways of using this language in order to attract their attention to a source outside themselves, presenting our interventions in ways that are non-threatening for that particular person.

- We have to be alert to any new material that people bring, and be aware of the need for surprise to 'keep the door open'.

- Above all, we need to remember that the aim of our interactions is to be present for an individual in a way which opens up the person to the possibilities of new experience.

We are trying to enlarge their arena so that they become aware of a wider world outside their own and begin to see it as an interesting and pleasurable place to be. We need to share ourselves in ways the person finds safe in order to give them the confidence to explore further.

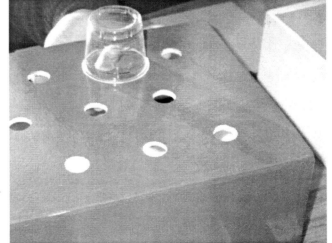

'Catch my finger'

Chapter Three

USING THE PERSON'S LANGUAGE

Once we are confident of the way we are working in the arena and understand its language and boundaries, we can begin to use it more deliberately. For example, we can enhance relationships and make it easier for others to communicate.

> **MARIA**, a young woman with Rett's syndrome, makes sounds and her family makes sounds back to her.
>
> Although Maria smiled, she wasn't really engaged until I suggested that her family mirrored her sounds more closely. She immediately 'came to life' in a way they had not seen before. A friend of the family was also able to have what she described as a most amazing conversation with Maria over the telephone. The responses were not dependent on the friend being present, only on their mutual pleasure and exploration of Maria's language.

Defusing distress

Thinking in terms of helping a person rather than controlling their disturbed behaviour, we can sometimes use a person's language to distract them and move their attention away from their inner turmoil (where they appear to have got stuck in a stereotypic mode which feeds itself and builds up into self-injury or outwardly directed aggression) back to relating to the outside world. Since noticing this, I have been paying particular attention to ways of using personal codes to defuse distressed behaviours (which are potentially, at least, and sometimes actually, spiralling out of control) focusing the person back on the outside world.

When we discussed the relationship between surprise and habituation (see page 20), we saw how, by combining the elements of Fran's 'inside' and 'outside' languages, staff were able to divert Fran's attention from her disturbed inner state. The following histories illustrate the use of the same technique with people with disabilities ranging through the wide spectrum from profound disability to Asperger's syndrome.

COLIN, who has very severe learning difficulties and severe autism, periodically gets very distressed. He shouts and becomes very agitated, sweats profusely and paces up and down.

I am asked to see Colin when he is already disturbed. Sitting away from him, I reflect back his sounds. When he hears, he becomes calmer and within five minutes he is reclining on the floor in his relaxed position. With normal intervention, it takes fifteen minutes before he calms down.

CASSIE, who has Asperger's syndrome, tells me that she is making meat sandwiches for her supper. She then slips into a repetitive and increasingly agitated mode, which involves the importance to her of the number seven. Her voice rises and rises as she becomes more distressed.

I use the actual word Cassie has told me is significant to her and ask her if she is going to have *seven* meat sandwiches for supper. She looks at me in surprise and laughs, 'No, three.' She turns back to making her supper. I have used Cassie's language, her personal code, to enter the closed world of her stereotype and draw her attention back to the preparation of her meal.

MARK, who has very severe learning disabilities, self-injures, hitting his head. He strokes his cheek with a circular movement when he is becoming upset.

Mark shows interest when I echo his movement, first on myself and then on his cheek. When he is becoming disturbed, it is possible to distract him by drawing attention to a source of 'his' touch which comes from outside himself.

JANET, who has very severe autism, attacks people when she is upset. She speaks in a high, sing-song voice and speaks of herself in the third person. The recognisable onset of her distress is marked by her eyes becoming staring and darting about, by distinctive hum-cries and finally her hands going up as her cries get louder. Sometimes she will run and turn off the radio or TV before she attacks.

Continued…

When Janet starts her eye movements and cries, I sit down and reflect her cries back to her. She runs and turns off the TV, then returns and looks at me with surprise on her face. She says to me, in a low voice, 'You be me!' (By this she means 'You copy me' as she will often say, 'Janet be Mary!' and then copy her.) I have been able to reach Janet by using her own signs that are part of her inner language. She answers me from her inner self with a voice that sounds completely different and more centred than the usual high childish voice which she uses. She also uses the first person.

Stress can build up as an outcome of a person being unable or not allowed to do what they want. They cannot control their world.

When **MAJELLA** gets on the coach to go home from her day centre, her escort is warned that she is becoming upset and there may be difficulties. She is muttering to herself about wanting to stay in that evening – she doesn't want to go out. She becomes increasingly repetitive, agitated and locked into her stress: 'I will **not** go out; *I will stay in and turn on the TV and watch EastEnders!*

At this stage, Majella usually becomes physically aggressive but her escort picks up what is, for Majella, the most important word and puts it in another light: 'Yes,' she says, 'EastEnders – that's an interesting programme.'

This use of Majella's actual words, picking up the subject that is important to her in another context, catches her attention and diverts her interest to a discussion about the programme.

In her book, *Autism: Preparing for Adulthood*, Howlin observes that:

> 'Direct attempts to prevent or prohibit obsessional or ritual behaviours result in individuals becoming more disturbed, agitated and anxious. If stopped, they may develop new rituals and obsessions. As they become larger, attempts to prevent these activities become more difficult.' [14]

However, there is sometimes the alternative of working *through* repetitive and some disturbed behaviours in a creative way which reduces anxiety. In particular, all the people described above responded to the use of their personal code by moving from their inner world, where they were so upset, to a more positive context outside themselves. By *using their language*, it was possible to enter their arena and draw their attention away from their inner distress. We were able to divert each person from their stereotype by reducing stress, even when the person was already involved in or building up to challenging behaviour, bringing them down to the point of re-entry into 'this world'.

If we are to speculate as to *why* mirroring a person's exact activity or words when they are becoming disturbed should offer the possibility of being able to divert them from their outbursts, we need to look back at the processes which are taking place in that person:

- There is turmoil in their inner world. If they have autistic tendencies, we know from what they tell us that, for whatever reason, when they are stressed, their processing becomes overloaded and the images and sounds their senses are receiving fragment and distort. This is a distressing and painful process, one that some people describe as agony:

  'I would do anything to stop it, run out into the middle of the road, bash my head against a wall,' Weekes.[15]

- The person may be trying to cut down or control sensory input. Williams[12] says that she cuts out processing one sense in order to be able to cope with input to others. An alternative is to limit the volume of the input, as with Janet who, when she is becoming distressed, turns off the radio or TV before she attacks.

As has been pointed out, making use of the critical words or actions on which a person is focused introduces surprise and draws attention away from their inner turmoil to the outside world. At this crucial stage, empathy is probably not enough – just saying, 'You must feel miserable', or similar words may not penetrate: the interaction must be a word or action which relates critically to the person's inner language at the present time. (It may be that when we become locked into anger and anguish – as is possible for all of us – we mentally return to the infant stage where we need a 'parent' figure to confirm our exact words before we move on.*)

While the primary intention of person-to-person intervention is not to 'manage' challenging behaviour but to help the person feel good about themselves, where there is a relatively slow build-up to the challenging behaviour, this approach does seem to offer the possibility of a respectful and non-threatening way of intervention with some people who are disturbed. There are some indications, however, that this type of approach is less likely to be effective where the disturbed behaviour is linked to temporal-lobe epilepsy.

Interpreting sounds

We often experience many practical difficulties when trying to disentangle a language which involves a whole range of sounds:

---

* Far-fetched as this may seem, a friend related a parallel personal experience when locked in to a road-rage situation: it needed mirroring of the actual significant words in a sympathetic context and, hence, acknowledgement of the specific feeling, to release him from his anger.

- what is the function of each?

- what, if anything, is the person trying to say?

- are the sounds outwardly-directed attempts to communicate, to let us know what the person wants, as, for example, in screams related to events?

- are the sounds inwardly directed, aimed at self-stimulation? Is the person talking to herself?

- are the sounds non-intentional, such as the clicking noise made by a person's jaws when eating?

Even non-intentional noises can be used as part of a person's language – especially if associated with a pleasant activity. The next history illustrates this point.

HANNAH has severe cerebral palsy and no sight. In the day centre, she screams at dinner, when she is in the hoist, and when she is about to travel on the coach. The screaming at dinner is a particular problem as it upsets other students.

One view is that Hannah needs to be helped to learn to wait for her dinner, perhaps by finding ways of distracting her. Alternatively, we can try to see how her day looks to her.

Some people with cerebral palsy seem to be very hungry. In Hannah's case, food is the most important thing in her life. She is only really happy when her stomach is full. When she reaches the dining room, she can smell the food but, because she is blind, cannot see the preparations for its arrival. Often there is a long wait, ten to fifteen minutes. Hannah becomes increasingly distressed. By the time she is served, she is screaming loudly.

Hannah is fed by spoon and eats fast – then there is another ten-minute wait before her dessert arrives, something she particularly enjoys as she has a sweet tooth. So Hannah screams again. This is communication. She is telling us what she wants.

The situation can be resolved by making sure that Hannah is not moved to the dining area until her food is ready, and also by making sure that there is no delay between the first and second course. We then see the situation from the point of view of a person who is blind and hungry and unable to know that her meal is on the way. We adapt to her needs.

Continued...

Hannah also screams when she is lifted, either manually or in the hoist. Watching this, I notice the look of sheer terror going over her face when she is lifted, even though the staff who lift her are careful and very gentle. Her reaction suggests pain and the fear of pain. The latter can be just as upsetting as pain itself – a blueprint in the mind which, as a result of some past incident, is painful enough to cause spasm when Hannah is being lifted. (Jolliffe[10] says, *'Fear has dominated my life. Even when things are not directly threatening, I tend to fear something horrible may happen.'*)

When Hannah is eating, which she likes, her jaw makes a clicking sound.

She is fascinated when I use these clicks as a way of distracting her during periods when she is normally afraid – for example, before getting on the hoist at the back of the coach and when she is being lifted – to the extent that it overrides her fear of being lifted. She is quiet during the period of departure, a time when she usually screams. The clicking is part of her most positive internal sensation – eating.

As well as her communication screams, telling us what she wants or dislikes, Hannah also has non-intentional sounds which are part of her repertoire. She recognises them and, since they are associated with her most pleasurable activity, we can use them to remind her of this and calm her when she is afraid.

To summarise:

The approach which I use starts off with extremely careful and non-judgmental observation:

- what *exactly* is going on for this person?
- how can we learn from the person what their own true needs are, as opposed to our needs of them?
- how can we meet these needs and start to enrich their lives?

Chapter Four

GETTING THE BALANCE RIGHT

There are two questions that are sometimes raised.

1 Doesn't working with repetitive behaviour sometimes reinforce the stereotype?

In practice, the answer seems to be 'no'. On the contrary, picking up the person's own signals and reflecting them back from outside their arena shifts their focus outward from the core self; that is, the person looks outside themselves for the source of the stimuli which they have been giving themselves. As in the infant learning process, the external source confirms the core self so that the core self is able to move on and explore further. By handing over control, letting the person lead the 'conversation', we open up for them the possibility of understanding that what they do can affect how we, and those around them, respond. If we do not give people this opportunity, they may never be able to move on from pre-intentional language, whatever form it takes, to intentional language – using their signals deliberately for communication. People need to take this step in order to break out of the stereotype.

Far from enhancing the stereotype, reflecting back a person's repetitive behaviour almost always helps them to become relaxed. As the tension eases, they slow down and become more able to be flexible and interact. The area of negotiation enlarges. As their confidence increases, they are prepared to consider and try out new activities and let themselves be opened to new experiences.

2 Isn't it better to leave them in 'their' world?

It is not always possible to predict the outcome of bringing a person from 'their world' to 'this world'. As they emerge, they begin to take an interest in their environment. People who empty cupboards and strip leaves from houseplants present more of a challenge to their support staff than those who sit quietly. The increasing confidence to explore, on their part, may test our resolution as we begin to learn the consequences of empowerment.

Furthermore, it is sometimes extremely difficult to disentangle 'disturbed behaviour' from the way we work with people. With the best intentions in the world, our engagements with a person may reinforce their problems. For example, it is hard not to feel singled out when someone, who does not know how to relate normally, picks on you as a particular member of support staff and follows you round all day, sniffing your hair. However, using words such as 'attention seeking' does not address an individual's need to find appropriate ways of making contact.

I want to examine the next history in detail, not because I was able to offer any startling remedies, but to illustrate how important it is to look at all of a person's difficulties from their point of view. Although the work we did with Sunita was in some ways beneficial, in others it presented staff with increased care problems.

SUNITA shouts loudly and repeatedly and disturbs the neighbours. To attract attention, she puts her face close to staff and makes her noise. Sometimes she brings them a cup and, if they fail to take it, she drops it. She has a number of less obvious repetitive behaviours and slides from one to the next. She has a very short memory and seems to be losing skills. It is suggested that Sunita is sliding into senility.

Firstly, the overall impression was that, although staff liked Sunita, almost all the signals she received from them were negative because of the difficulties of being with her. For example, when she came to them, they turned their heads away. Picking on a particular member of staff was known as 'targeting', so that even the language reinforced their feeling of being a 'victim'.

We decided to try to alter this to give Sunita the attention she so clearly desired. When she put her face near, staff smiled, said 'Hello' and, using one of her own behaviours, rubbed her cheek gently with a finger. Staff were encouraged to think of targeting as an opportunity for interaction and take advantage of it.

It was difficult to work with Sunita through Intensive Interaction as, apart from her noises, to which she did not respond when they were echoed back to her, she had a number of different repetitive behaviours. She slid from one to another and in practice it was difficult to know whether she had stopped because she was listening and waiting to see what would happen, or if she was starting another one; it was difficult to know where she 'was' at any particular time.

Continued…

We did, however, find that Sunita was sometimes responsive to our joining in with her finger-scratching, a behaviour which was not at all obvious but did go on most of the time. Working from this, I tried using vibration on the area Sunita was self-stimulating and from this was able to lead on to using a food-mixer, power-sander and vacuum cleaner, all of which vibrated in the area of her hand which she normally self-stimulated. (Previous attempts to persuade Sunita to help with vacuuming had foundered on the expectation that she should show prolonged interest in it. We have to remember that the whole point of an interactive approach is to provide opportunities for doing things *together* rather than teaching people to do things by themselves: it is about relationship and not skills.) Further, when staff looked more closely at Sunita's movements, they realised that while she was unable to manoeuvre the machine backwards and forwards, she could manage to push it straight up the corridor. Their careful observation turned her efforts to success.

Another activity which related to Sunita's self-stimulation of her fingers was rubbing cream into her hands. Staff found this very effective in calming her.

Looking at language, ours and hers, it was apparent that at least some of Sunita's loud noises derived from words. Staff were asked to look out for approximating sounds and encourage her if she used them. She also had some high sounds which were happy noises from bits of song. She liked it if these were sung back to her.

Sentences needed to be very clear, for example, we used nouns and not pronouns: 'put the cup in the sink,' but not, 'put it there.'

Sunita's memory was very short. She needed reminding frequently as she would forget she was carrying a cup and drop it. If she did drop it, we picked it up, gave it back and made a game of passing it one to another, gradually extending the time she held it.

The immediate outcome of this change in care was that Sunita became more interested in her surroundings. In some ways, her care became more difficult as she started to investigate things she had never noticed before, such as taking things off shelves. Nor did her sounds diminish. However, Sunita smiled and made happy noises more frequently. There were periods when she was quiet. She was able to carry things for short distances and, with prompt, put them in appropriate places. The staff took a more positive view of her.

I have included this more detailed account because I want to highlight that it is not just enough to look at a particular behaviour in isolation. We need to look at the whole person and how we *interact* with each other, altering each other's behaviour.

The important points are:

- it may be difficult to succeed with Intensive Interaction when a person has a series of repetitive behaviours – as they pass from one to another, it is not always clear whether they are attending or moving on

- it may be important to take a positive view of attention-seeking and find appropriate and acceptable ways to give a person the attention they need

- it is important to analyse a complex situation from the point of view of the difficulties a person experiences rather than the problems they present

- people with short memories need constant reminders.

To return to the question of whether or not it would be better to leave people in their own world, there is also the philosophical component. Can I say, for someone else, that my world is better than their world? I think most of us would agree that we are born social animals. Evidence suggests that we do not reach our full potential if we are reared isolated. Certainly, I have come across two people (in whom epilepsy was not well-controlled) where intervention *has* had counter-productive effects. For example, one woman has a severe seizure every time she smiles; her physical condition makes interaction difficult if not impossible. Such situations are, however, extremely rare. The vast majority of people respond with interest, warmth, reaching out, smiles, laughter and most often they are relaxed during and after interventions. As well as this, even people with profound disabilities, although they may get tired and need time to assimilate their new-found experiences, usually come back showing evidence of wanting to continue, both at the time and on follow-up occasions.

We also have direct evidence from Donna Williams, who has severe autism, as to what her inner world feels like. In the very revealing Channel 4 programme, *Jam-Jar*, she explains her poem *Nobody Nowhere*:

> 'Autism is…total withdrawal into yourself, the whole world is torn up and made redundant. You have replaced every relationship that you could have had with the people in the world and they don't matter any more … there is no sense of "where" and no sense of "who" and if you are compelled to live in there, you live in fear.
>
> 'The wind can grow cold in the depths of your soul,
> where nothing can hurt you until it's too late.' [12]

These moving descriptions of her inner world not only speak to people with autism but remind us all of our own inward places, our private arena in which we feel safe but which we may also need to defend. At this end of the scale of social interaction, we have the stereotype, locked in to self-stimuli. The whole aim of the work I am describing is to reach into the core self and build up a person's confidence to the point where they no longer feel threatened and so the boundary between core self and core other can become more permeable (see page 7). On the other hand, those people who have lost their sense of boundaries will need help to redefine these (see page 7). Either way, the aim is not just to enlarge the core self (where the person has been able to integrate their new experience) but also to strengthen the person's capacity for negotiating relationship. I need to feel stronger in myself so I can reach out to you.

However, getting the balance right between leaving a person in their world and encouraging them to come to ours is not always easy. Their world feels safe, a place to which they can retreat. Williams[12] talks about the strain of always trying to be in a world which does not understand her 'way of thinking'. The perimeter may be a place to erect defences – protecting a person from a world in which they are vulnerable. But it is also a prison which cuts out the possibility of reciprocal communication and the opportunities for giving and receiving affection, bonding and love.

Chapter Five

FINDING THE
RIGHT APPROACH

In order to get in touch with a person, we may not only need to take account of their language but also the difficulties they experience in processing our approaches – particularly the feelings which people with autistic tendencies may have. Such people will often be overwhelmed by what we imagine to be our normal or even valuing interventions.

How can we ensure that our presentation of a person's language is in a form they find acceptable?

Hypersensitivities

For example, what happens when we speak to a man who is hypersensitive to sound?

BEN, a resident in a community home, is very shy and easily upset. When he is upset, he attacks people. He frequently wanders round saying, 'Shut up, shut up!'

This is the sort of language of which we very often do not take much notice, thinking perhaps that it is just something the person has picked up in a previous institution – it is 'just something they say'. By thinking about Ben's difficult behaviour and relating it to shouting and loud noises, the house manager realises that Ben is using his limited language to try to get people to be quieter, that loud noise is intolerable for him. When the staff start to speak softly to him, there is a marked reduction in his outbursts.

It is very difficult for us to step outside our own sensory experience and the tight blueprints we carry round with us of how the world 'ought' to be. It needs conscious effort on our behalf and we need frequent reminding. We need genuinely to listen to what people are saying, otherwise we can get it wrong for them.

Most people who work with people with autism are familiar with gaze avoidance. The person will do anything to avoid looking at us. They turn their head away or give fleeting glances and then their eyes slip away. We need to listen to what they are saying.

> *'People do not appreciate how unbearably difficult it is for me to look at a person. It disturbs my quietness and is terribly frightening,'* Jolliffe.[10]

Some people with autism find direct eye contact acutely painful. Because we are so dependent on eye contact ourselves, this is difficult for us to understand and very often we try to insist that they look at us.

The next history illustrates how respecting and being sensitive to this difficulty can make it possible to communicate with a person who appeared to be totally unreachable.

PAULA spends much of her time in her room. She becomes very disturbed, breaking furniture and attacking people. She avoids eye contact and does not like strangers.

When I go to see Paula, she is sitting on her bed, twisting her hair. She looks away from me. I deliberately avoid looking at her directly, gazing out of the window, and I twist my hair. After a while I say, using indirect speech, 'If I had been doing this for some time, I should want to brush my hair, and if I wanted to brush my hair, I should put my hairbrush on the bed.' She puts her hairbrush on the bed. I walk over to her and brush her hair, still looking out of the window and speaking indirectly. After about five minutes, Paula leans forward and rests her head against me. The occupational therapist, who has been trying for months to help Paula learn to make tea using behavioural techniques, uses the same indirect technique the following day. Paula makes tea with minimal prompt (she needs help to take the lid off the tea-caddy) and ends up hugging her therapist.

Paula wants to make contact and is able to do so when we use an indirect approach, respecting the overload and fragmentation that she experiences when people look at her and address her directly. Her sensory input breaks up and her nervous system feeds back pain instead of information. Looking away and speaking indirectly is non-threatening and allows Paula to communicate.

It is quite difficult to adopt this approach and requires practice. Support staff will say that they feel cold or rude if they do not look at the person to whom they are speaking, or if they use indirect speech or simplify the language they use (this is not the same as using childish language).

However, Williams[5] says that far from experiencing such consideration as impersonal, she was grateful when people respected her difficulties.

Sometimes people who are hypersensitive to sound or direct eye contact, can tolerate it under certain circumstances; for example, if they know that the sound or contact is going to happen and have time to prepare for what is coming, or if we are working inside their stereotype so that the signals we are giving them are recognisable and non-threatening. Under these circumstances, the person feels safe to negotiate. They can relax and may even initiate eye contact and touch themselves.

Boundaries

Part of the same problem for people with autism is not having a strong sense of boundary, the difference between core self and other. Returning to Williams,[8] if we do not know whether our hand belongs to ourselves, since we are switching off processing one or more of our senses in order to try to prevent overload, we have no picture of ourselves. We do not know where 'we' end and 'another person' begins. Under these circumstances, it is very easy to feel invaded by other. This is a very threatening situation and is illustrated by the next history, where Jack would like to communicate but needs a physical boundary between himself and another person in order to do so.

> **JACK**, who has severe autism, spends much of his time outside the house. He is very disturbed and runs away from people if they approach him. Occasionally he will come to the window and tap it. If anyone looks up, he laughs.
>
> Jack's behaviour suggests that he *does* want to communicate but can only do so if there is a physical screen between him and other people. This lets him know where they are and where he is. He can experience their separateness and therefore does not feel invaded. We decide to use a plastic screen to see if this will make it easier to get in touch with Jack. This is very successful. On the second visit, when we were not yet ready for him, Jack comes indoors, picks up the screen from the floor, puts it on the student's lap, knocks it and laughs at her. He is coming to us for the contact he enjoys which is now presented in a way he finds safe. He can knock and feel the physical boundary between us. It shows him, in a way which he can understand, that we are separate from him. He knows where he ends and we begin.

Such containment and separation may be built into the stereotype in more obvious ways; that is, the person uses the stereotype as the boundary to protect themselves from overload.

LUKE, who has autism, spends much of his time within doorways or moving from one paving stone to the next in a way which suggests that squares are safe; it is the children's game of lines and squares played in an obsessional way. In any other circumstances, he is extremely withdrawn and difficult to motivate.

On the assumption that Luke needs a frame to protect him, I make a game. This is a sheet of paper ruled with black lines in squares (as shown in the picture below). The aim of the game is to flick the pieces (flat, black lids) into the squares. If they land not touching the lines, then they are safe. If they overlap the lines they are not safe and I take them back and try again. At first, Luke controls my game by saying, 'Yes' or 'No' as to whether or not I can have a turn. This in itself is co-operation of a kind he is not normally able to show. Within twenty minutes, he is sitting at the table playing the game with us, dealing out the pieces and taking turns.

Working creatively within the arena of the stereotype, where he feels safe, contained and not threatened by overloading, Luke is able to interact. I would suggest that this has considerable implications for the way in which care is carried out for people with severe autism. By working within the stereotype, using the individual's own language, we can reduce the tensions caused by overloading. For example, Luke (in common with a number of other autistic people) seems to feel most threatened when he wakes in the morning. His confusion is greatest then. He runs from his bed and crouches in the corner of the room and refuses to come out and put on his clothes. Although, in this case, circumstances prevented my trying it out, the approach which I would suggest that might

help Luke is to provide a square rug with a black border and put his clothes in the centre, offering a clearly recognisable and safe place for him to dress.

It also helps a person if you tell them in advance when it is necessary for you to move into the area that they regard as their safe place.

The squares game

WILLIAM, who has De Lange syndrome, sits in the doorway to the kitchen and hits anyone who tries to pass through.

William clearly feels safe when he is framed by the doorway. I suggest that he feels threatened when his safe space is invaded. Staff stand away from him and call his name to get his attention when they need to get into the kitchen, pointing out by simple gestures what they need to do. When they do this, William no longer hits out.

When a person feels threatened by direct contact, it sometimes helps to divert their attention to equipment which contains elements of the familiar signals which constitute their language – a middle ground from which the threat has been removed.

PETER, who has autism and very severe behaviour problems, patrols the large day-room, licking the walls in three specific places. If this activity is interrupted, he becomes extremely disturbed and attacks anyone near him.

Peter enjoys objects which spin. I am able to attract his attention with a spinning mirror. He is happy to sit and operate this. Although this is less fraught than his previous activity, it is still a solitary occupation. I then introduce a puzzle which has spinning pieces but also requires manipulation to complete it (as shown in the picture below). Peter is interested in the spinning activity but cannot complete the puzzle by himself so he accepts my putting my hands on his to help him. By displacing our attention from the face-to-face interaction that he finds so threatening, and substituting the middle ground of the puzzle (which includes the activity in which he is interested), Peter is able to allow hands-on contact.

To summarise:

● It is not only the 'language' we use that is important, but also how we present it; not only *what* we say, but *how* we say it.

Rotating disc puzzle

Self-injury

We have to ask ourselves whether or not it is possible to use these techniques with people who are self-injuring. It may be part of a continuum but – at present – I want to differentiate between those people who are self-injuring as part of a repetitive behaviour pattern and those who injure themselves as a response to current external circumstances. As with sounds such as screaming, we need to know if the self-injury is rooted in internal factors or is a response to external events.

TARA, who has severe autism, is unable to make contact with people, except on occasional days when she follows them round sniffing their hair. She runs away from people and hits her cheek so hard that she lays the bone open. She is very disturbed.

I stand at the opposite end of the room so that Tara does not feel pressured by me. Every time she hits herself, I tap my cheek. It takes about twenty minutes before she sees me. When she does, she literally drops her jaw in surprise. She waits to see what I will do, so after a short interval I tap my cheek again. She bangs hers. I mirror her and in a short while she begins to introduce new varieties of movement with her arms and hands. When I get it right, she laughs. Then I move slowly towards her, tapping my cheek. Eventually, I am able to place my finger on Tara's cheek, opposite to the one she is hitting, and very gently echo her movements on her cheek. Tara's self-harm gradually becomes more gentle, mirroring the progressive quieting of my tap. Her keyworker becomes involved in working with Tara this way. Over the following months, Tara starts, of her own volition, to bring a cushion and sit beside her key-worker in the evenings instead of running away.

I am not suggesting that all self-injuring behaviour can be modified in this way as not enough work has been carried out in this particular field. However, that which I have done indicates that it is at least worth trying.

Again, the crucial stages are:

● finding the right language

● finding a non-threatening way to present it.

As was the case with Tara, it may then be possible to use the person's language creatively, drawing their attention more and more from their inner locked-in world to the world outside.

Getting the level right

Some people have special interests through which one can attract their attention. If these interests have not been developed or have been allowed to lapse, a person's behaviour can be very deceptive indeed – they may appear much less able than they potentially are, particularly if they have a hearing or visual disability.

> **An art therapist works with JOSH, whose sole interest appears to be counting beads. Efforts to interest him in alternative activities have been unsuccessful.**
>
> Josh does, however, have a hearing aid which he takes off to show to the therapist. She gets him to draw round it and enlarges it on the photocopier. This is traced onto card, used as the basis of a design and projected onto material for fabric painting. Josh's designs are shown in an exhibition in the community. He is very proud of this and takes people to show them. Using the personal object in which Josh is interested, the therapist has been able to lead him to a new way of relating to this world.

> **JEFF, who is blind and almost totally unresponsive, dislikes being touched. He is reputed to have enjoyed walking by the sea in the past when his mother was alive. He mutters but it is not intelligible.**
>
> Jeff comes to life when he is taken for a long walk on shingle (where he has to hold on) on a day when there is a wild wind and the waves are crashing. After two hours, he is obviously enjoying himself and suggests that they 'go for a lager'.

Both Josh and Jeff appeared to be unreachable. The battle with their sensory disabilities had overwhelmed them and they had retreated from the struggle, to the point where they appeared to be profoundly disabled. Only a very strong significant stimulus had brought them back to 'this world'.

Chapter Six

EQUIPMENT AND
INTERACTIVE ACTIVITIES

The actual way in which we decide to work with a person depends entirely on that individual. Either we can enter into their world and work with the non-threatening language which their brain recognises through Intensive Interaction or interactive activities, or we can try to find an alternative presentation which is more fascinating to them than their own signals. This would override the signals which they are using to talk to themselves as, for example, when we might try using vibration to desensitise a person who is continually scratching a particular part of themselves. In either case, we are trying to refocus the person's attention on an external signal so that they look outside themselves for its source. Which way we try depends on the person's behaviours and responses. In the end, a two-pronged strategy may be needed.

There comes a stage in the process of getting close to people where it may be useful to use equipment. We can use equipment:

- to **capture attention** by enhancing the stereotype or the person's interest so as to present it in a more compelling way

- to help **engage the attention** of people who find face-to-face interaction threatening.

The first two uses have already been explored, as in the history of Rose, who was examining dandruff (see page 10) and that of Peter, who found one-to-one intervention acceptable when his attention was focused on spinning objects (see page 43).
Additional reasons for introducing equipment are:

- to provide **extra tactile stimulation** for people with visual impairment

- to encourage particular **physical movements** or activities

- to provide **pleasure**, as in hobbies

- to encourage **sharing in social activities**

- to encourage and facilitate **communication**

- to help understand **abstract ideas** such as 'time'

- to assist people to have **access to feelings** which are too painful to experience in everyday life

- containment – to help people look after **precious objects** and to help them 'hold' ideas that are frightening

- to explore **nurturing**.

Extra tactile stimulation

A large proportion of the stimuli we receive from the outside world are visual. It is not only information which people with visual impairment miss out on. They actually need extra tactile stimulation. This can be given at a simple level with Astroturf, which has a springy, scratchy feeling which is interesting to touch.

Support staff think it may help CRAIG, who has a visual disability, if he has some idea of his body image. He spends most of his time sitting in a chair looking at the ceiling and rubbing his hands through his hair.

In order to help Craig look at a mirror, we need to alter the direction of his gaze. This involves getting his hands down from his head. Bearing in mind that Craig enjoys the feeling of rubbing his hands through his hair, we make a mirror with a strip of Astroturf on one end (as shown in the picture below) and place his hands on it. After a few prompts, Craig brings his hands down by himself and starts to explore this new texture. He then finds the mirror and starts to compare the crisp, springy feeling of the Astroturf with the smooth, shiny surface of the mirror, moving his hands from one to the other. As his head follows his hands down, Craig starts to peer at his image in the mirror.

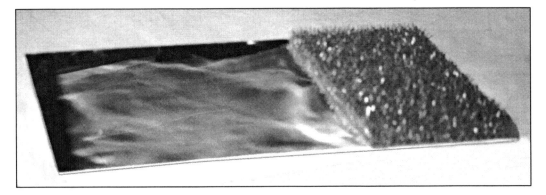

Astroturf mirror

Craig enjoys textures and comparing one with another. We should not have learned this unless we had stayed with his discovery of the Astroturf. It is crucial that we learn to resist the temptation to fast-forward into wider exploration. We have to stay with the person, sharing and enjoying their sense experience with them, in order to validate it.

At a more sophisticated level, tactile stimulation can be provided with three-dimensional puzzles of varying levels of difficulty.

CHARLIE, who is deaf-blind and very angry, comes down in the morning and hits people.

We make a difficult multi-layered three-dimensional puzzle for Charlie (as shown in the pictures below). He is totally absorbed by this. It breaks the pattern of being angry first thing in the morning, so that he has space to explore people and learn to relate to them in a different way.

Three-dimensional puzzle

Physical movements

It is always important to work in conjunction with other therapists. Sometimes, equipment can be designed to help with specific movements.

> **MATT** has stiff shoulders and his physiotherapist asks for equipment which will help.
>
> We fit a netball ring with tubular elastic bandage, so that when a ball is thrown in, it can only be withdrawn by pulling it through the tube. Matt finds this helpful.

> An occupational therapist asks for equipment to encourage **ROY** to stretch out his arms when they come out of splints.
>
> The problem is to find something in which Roy will be sufficiently interested to hold onto. He likes the feeling of corrugated tube over a bar, which we attach to a rope so that we can pull on it.

> **CALLUM**, who has cerebral palsy, has difficulty opening his hand and turning his wrist. It is not rigid: he has just given up using this hand as it is easier to use the other.
>
> By laying short lengths of narrow tube horizontally on the table, I am able to encourage Callum to pick them up and turn his wrist in order to place them over vertical pegs.

I find that when looking for suitable designs, it helps to enact the desired movements oneself repetitively. This tends to trigger related images which can be used to devise relevant equipment.

Individual pleasure

If we leave equipment with a person because they are enjoying it while we are not working with them, it loses its capacity as a vehicle of surprise and, consequently, its value as a way of getting in touch. The individual may become bored or fixated on the object.

However, there are some people with disabilities who delight in certain activities in the same way as we enjoy hobbies.

ROLAND, who has severe visual disabilities, loves looking through grids and perforated sheets and at patterns. They give him great pleasure and offer a new way for him to explore light and shadow. His mother says he enjoys them as much as a stamp collector enjoys his collection.

For Roland, offering new variations adds interest to his collection and to his life. It does not prevent his relating to people in his quiet way.

Sharing in social activities

Some people are physically not able to play games such as snooker or table tennis. In day centres they stand or sit near others, watching while they are playing – they are excluded by their lack of co-ordination. If they do manage to hit the ball, it goes into the net or off the table. These difficulties can be overcome by clamping a four-by-one-inch wooden batten down the length of each side of the table – the ends are left open (see *Diagram 2* and picture overleaf). These battens can be fitted to any rectangular table, or square tables pushed together. (The clamp only fastens on the underside of the table and therefore does not harm the table's surface.) Table tennis bats are used, or, if the person has difficulty in holding these at the right angle, it is easy to design bats using door-handles or special grips. Ball size is varied as appropriate – a yellow tennis ball is easy to see.

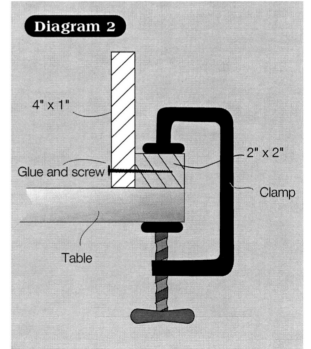

Diagram 2

4" x 1"

Glue and screw

2" x 2"

Clamp

Table

'Pushball' makes a good game which is enjoyed at many levels (see the pictures overleaf). It can be played quickly or slowly, depending on capability. The ball is either hit straight down or spun off the sides. Pushball is useful for promoting tracking, and hand-eye co-ordination. It can be set up on dining room tables and is easy to use by people in wheelchairs. It is also great fun. It has been very helpful in promoting self-control with one individual who learned that if he returned the ball in such a way that his less able peers were able to return it, he would get a better game than if he smashed it. He learned to co-operate.

'Pushball'

Communication

Before discussing the design of equipment related to communication, we need to look more specifically at the problems which people have in getting in touch with each other.

All the people who are the subject of this book have communication difficulties – for one reason or another they cannot 'talk' to us and we cannot 'talk' to them. This cuts out the possibilities of telling each other what we want or do not want, giving or asking for information, making comments or communicating emotion. Because of the frustrations involved, many people become withdrawn or exhibit what we call 'challenging behaviour' when they try to let us know that they are in situations which they cannot handle.

When we are working with people, we very often tend to focus on our need to convey information to them and lose sight of their need to tell us what they want and how they feel. It is vital, not only to find the most effective means of talking to a person, but also to learn to observe their body language so that we begin to understand what the person is feeling and trying to tell us.

To be real, communication is a two-way process.

1 How do we let the person know our needs of them?

First, there are the barriers such as in hearing loss, or processing difficulties as in people with autism:

'They may hear sounds but cannot attach meaning to them,' Peeters.[16]

Also, people may not understand that speech is directed to them or even understand what speech is for:

'Speech is no more significant than any other sound,' Jolliffe.[10]

In actual practice, it may sometimes be difficult to distinguish between people with learning disabilities who also have severe hearing loss and people with learning disabilities who also have autism. However, the difference may be crucial when we try to communicate: people with autism may find it extremely difficult, if not impossible, to make sense of sign language – it is too abstract, they just cannot make the connection.

In his comprehensive book on autism, Peeters[16] makes it clear that in order to make ourselves understood, we need the closest possible visual link between the gesture by which the message is conveyed and the intention we are trying to get over. In order to let a person know I want to go into the kitchen, I point first to myself and then indicate the kitchen. Peeters also points out that **the method we use to communicate with each other must be the one that is the most efficient in enabling a particular individual to make a connection with the world around them**. It should not be chosen for any other reason.

For some people, even objects of reference (object clues which relate to a proposed activity) may be too abstract if they do not relate closely enough to the message content. We may have to make our communication clues even simpler.

● *Objects of reference plus gesture*
These should be clues from a familiar part of the proposed activity from the person's immediate surroundings rather than a representation. For example, if a person was going for a walk, the difference here might be between their coat (a direct visual clue) or some representational object such as tree bark.

The object of reference needs to be supported by a simple gesture such as pointing from the person to the door.

● *Demonstration*
Some people with autism cannot do something, even if they want to, unless they have a model to copy. They actually need to see an activity done. Demonstration involves actually showing a person what is required. If we take the example of making toast, the visual clue

and gesture might be holding a slice of bread and indicating the toaster. Demonstration would involve actually showing the person the act of putting the toast in the toaster so that they can copy the action by putting their slice in the other side.

- *Demonstration with hands-on prompt*

Some people will actually need physical hands-on prompt – doing it together. There are advantages to this: it can be seen as a chance for sharing an activity and so not only convey the information but also give an opportunity for 'being together'.

Some people with autism hear what we are saying but need time to process it before they can understand it and organise a reply. Jolliffe, who has autism but is very able, tells us:

> 'Sometimes when I really need to speak, the words won't come out and the frustration
> is terrible. I want to kick out at people and objects, throw things, rip things up and
> break them and very occasionally, scream.' [10]

In my own experience, this time-lag, while the person is trying to process what we are saying, can be up to a matter of hours. We have to understand the struggle that people are going through as they try to wrestle meaning into sound, and be patient and admire their tenacity. Their struggle shows us just how important it is for human beings to talk to each other.

2 What is the person trying to say to us?

When people have no speech, we have to learn to watch their body language and what it tells us of their needs. This requires very careful observation.

The following case history is of a woman with autism.

When **BRENDA** is thirsty, she flicks the teapot to indicate that she wants tea. At her key-worker's house, although there is a teapot, she flicks the kettle as she knows that, in this house, tea is made with tea-bags.

In her bath, she tries to drink the water. When she starts, her key-worker immediately gives her a drink of iced water. This satisfies her thirst but, being cold, is difficult to gulp. She now drinks what she wants and hands the glass back, sometimes with some water left in it.

It is crucial that we take notice of people's needs, not only because it is what they need but also because it is a way of letting them know that they can affect what we do – it begins to show people what communication is for. This is something we take for granted but is one of the many difficulties which people with autism experience: they do not understand that we can influence one another by talking to each other.

Communication is not only about conveying information but also about expressing feeling. People with autism have such difficulties with this that it has often been assumed that they do not experience any feelings. What is becoming apparent, however, is that they are able to experience and express emotions if we are working in a non-threatening way inside their arena, the area where they feel safe. This is often the outcome of using Intensive Interaction or interactive activities, as in the continuation of Brenda's history:

> **Brenda, who is very anxious and often agitated, makes sounds in her throat. I copy their rhythm by knocking on the table. At first she gets up and walks around. I only knock when she is sitting. When I get her attention, I gradually lean forward and knock across the table towards her. Eventually, Brenda looks up, smiles and puts out her hand and takes mine gently. She does this three times before she has had enough and walks away.**

This spontaneous gesture is a more meaningful gesture than a learned sign with which Brenda does not emotionally connect. We need to give people the opportunities to express their affection.

Continuing this history, we can see the importance of negotiation:

> **Brenda likes to go out but she has 'good days' and 'bad days'. Some time before it is time to go out, her key-worker puts on her own coat to give Brenda the idea of going out. She watches to see if Brenda is interested or whether she fidgets and walks away. If she is looking, she offers Brenda her coat – if Brenda pushes it away, her key-worker still keeps her coat on as it is important to keep the options open.**
>
> The key-worker needs to get the balance right between doing activities and not doing anything at all. However, negotiation does involve accepting when Brenda really does not want to go this time. This means that **getting her agreement has to take priority over timetables**. Brenda needs to know that when she makes it clear, through her way of communicating, that she does *not* want to go out today, we will take notice; what she does influences what we do and she has control.

We may need to be very careful about the meaning we attach to people's responses.

SUSHMA, who is easily frustrated and upset, gives clear signs for 'yes' and 'no'. However, careful observation of an incident where she indicates 'no' (she does not want the foot spa but immediately becomes upset when it is removed) suggests that she is not always getting these signs right. This is followed up by further observation by staff. It appears that while Sushma knows what a question is and that it requires an answer, she is either not understanding as well as was thought or she has not attached consistent meaning to her responses.

To help Sushma with this, staff now follow asking a question by giving her a second chance: for example, partially moving the foot spa away from her to a position where she can still see it and then turning back and asking her again. This helps Sushma to attach meaning to the question – it shows her what is going to happen.

Negotiation is about getting agreement. It is not enough to ask a person to do something. We must frame the question so that we secure acknowledgement before we start, so that together we take part in a process with which they connect. Then, the activity becomes theirs, not something that just happens to them. Agreement may be only a flicker of the eyes or a fractional nod – but, if we can obtain it, we shall accomplish the activity in a way that is sharing and being together, rather than caring (us doing something for, or to, them).

Making choices

Difficulties sometimes arise when social ideals are translated blanket-fashion without due attention to individual need. A classic example of this is the insistence on the use of choices for some people with autistic tendencies. Unfortunately, while based on the admirable premise that such people must be given control of their lives, the very act of being given a choice can set up a painful conflict. Under these circumstances, failure to process can lead to fragmentation, the outcome of which may be self-harm or attack.

Implementing such policies can translate into staff feeling that they are obliged to insist on individuals making a choice. For example, the question 'Do you want to go shopping or swimming?' can lead to the following outcomes:

- the person says 'swimming' because that is the last word in the sentence and the only one they could decode from the jumble of sound. Actually, they wanted to go shopping and are upset when it does not happen

- there is a long delay while the person tries to process the question

- the person has an outburst because they are unable to process the question.

We need to look extremely carefully at exactly what we are doing and to what extent any particular individual can be empowered by choice. There are degrees of choice, complex or simple.

- There is the either/or question:

  'Will you wear these shoes or these?'

- Or the simple question:

  'Will you wear these shoes?'

  And, if they are rejected, the question is repeated with another pair.

However, there is another type of choice, which we do not always think about, which really does hand over control to the individual, empowering them because it recognises – and shows them that we recognise – their inner difficulties. It centres on the problems they have with boundaries and gives them control over where we are in relation to them and how close we come. I am talking here about those people with autism who have trouble with other people:

'People...come in bits,' Barron.[9]

Such a situation, where an individual does not know where they end and another person begins, or which bits are theirs and which belong elsewhere, is invasive and threatening.

With a number of such people, those who are able to process some speech with the aid of gesture, I have found that letting them know that one respects their difficulties by asking such yes/no questions as, for example, 'May I come in?', pointing from myself to inside the room, or, 'May I sit down?', indicating a chair, are very much appreciated. Perhaps because it is non-invasive and prepares them for what I am about to do, this approach does not set up stress and is therefore easier to process.

Interaction with others

We have a tendency to think of communication in terms of interaction as a process that happens between 'them' (disabled) and ourselves (non-disabled). Equally important is the ability to interact with peers.

The lives of a group of people with profound and multiple disability are dominated by the continuous and unacceptably loud noises made by one of them, EILEEN. Eileen's noises distress other members of the group as well as staff – it is hard to work with the group against this background.

Continued...

> Working interactively through a kazoo, Eileen's sounds become more cheerful; she is obviously enjoying the exchanges, pausing to reflect between sounds, smiling and laughing. A video of the session highlights the effect it is having on other members of the group.
>
> Another woman, who is quadriplegic, is sitting with her head slumped down. She is often distressed by noises. During this session, she lifts her head and starts to echo them back. **She is smiling as she and Eileen talk to each other.** Other members of the group start to laugh. Another woman, who is normally shy, takes the kazoo and succeeds in blowing it. She laughs when she is applauded by the group and starts to play to her audience.

The difference in the quality of interaction and the 'feel' of the room is marked; it has changed from the expression of individual aloneness to group enjoyment. People are interacting with their peers deliberately.

Visual aids

There are some communication difficulties which can be helped by simple visual aids. I want to focus here on the design and presentation of these aids, which can be crucial to success.

> **LAURENCE confuses his name with his brother's – or possibly himself with his brother.**
>
> Laurence is helped to sort this out by making a two-piece jigsaw, which is all he can manage, from a photograph of himself and his brother sitting on a wall beside each other. By this means, he can see and name himself, together and apart from his brother, and he quickly learns to name himself.

As has been pointed out, the ability to process and comprehend can be sporadic, particularly in people with autism. This can mislead support staff into thinking that a person is lazy or difficult because they understood 'last time'. Often, such people are helped by flash-cards, a visual presentation of the request, which reinforce the message. These can be made of 1mm styrene sheet which can be cut with scissors. These cards can be kept handy in a bum-bag.

A number of people with cerebral palsy have communication boards which are too large to fit in their wheelchairs. As a consequence, the boards are often left unused on shelves. It is possible to make books which contain their pictographs out of styrene or foamex. The latter is an attractive material in brilliant colours which can be cut and drilled like plywood. Designing the stiff pages with staggered flanges makes them easy to turn (see the picture below). Bound with split rings, these books can be fastened to the wheelchairs by a chain so that they are always available.

Good design must be individually tailored to the requirements of an individual. It is not only the idea which is important but how it is delivered, since success may depend on it. As well as considering health and safety issues, we need to ask ourselves which materials will be the most visually attractive, which design will be the most easily manipulated and which will be most likely to convey the message we want to help the person understand.

Abstract ideas

Many people with learning disabilities do not understand the idea of time. It is an abstract concept and without it, their experience of reality is extremely confused.

> 'There is no sense of "where" – I never got the whole picture of who I am today, where I'm going tomorrow,' Williams.[12]

> 'Reality ... is a confusing interacting mass of events, places, sounds and sights. There seem to be no clear boundaries, order or meaning to anything. A large part of my life is spent trying to work out the pattern behind everything,' Jolliffe.[10]

> 'When I woke, I needed to know what was going to happen or there were tantrums,' Weekes.[15]

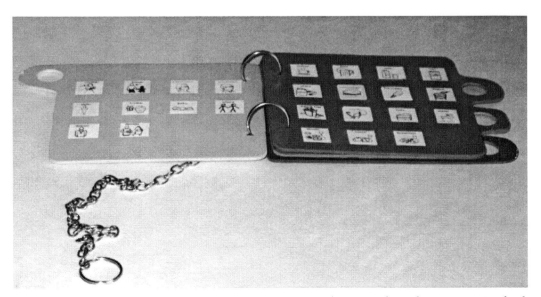

Flanged communication book

Peeters[16] discusses at length the need for structure presented in an intelligible way and points out that it is not only children with autism who benefit from it: it is also adults with autism and many adults with learning disabilities who do not also have autism. They need help to know who is coming when, what is going to happen and how long it will take.

If a person has speech, it is usually quite easy to spot when time is a problem for them. Although the person may be able to say the appropriate words – such as 'summer', 'tomorrow', 'this afternoon' – they may have absolutely no concept of the linear sequence and intervals of time. However, they *will* ask the questions, often again and again, 'Who's on tomorrow?' 'When's the bus coming?' and so on. No matter how often their question is answered, it does not address their anxiety. The event that is uppermost in their minds is not happening and they have no way of anticipating when it will. The answer to their question does not mean anything to them that they can grasp. 'Soon' is just a sound with no meaning attached. All they do know is that there is a gap between what they need to happen – for example, the presence of someone they rely on – and the fact that it is not happening *now*. The person is absent or present; it is an all-or-nothing situation. People often become progressively more disturbed as their anxiety rises. The anxiety which accompanies a lack of grasp of time is sometimes at the root of behaviour we see as challenging.

In her book, Howlin says:

> 'Repetitive questioning is the consequence of not understanding. Sometimes
> rephrasing helps but more often the information needs to be supplied in a
> non-verbal form such as photographs.'[14]

As has been already discussed under **Communication** (page 52), we may have to look for even simpler ways of getting in touch. We need to find which level of presentation helps a person most.

The specific design of equipment may be crucial to comprehension and we need to ask ourselves if the important features are visually outstanding and presented so that the sequence is clear. Will the person understand which way to follow it?

The following histories illustrate some of the ways which have been used successfully to help people who have difficulties with time.

Year

> **ALEX**, who has cerebral palsy (but not autism), is very disturbed when he hears the word 'holiday'. He thinks it means that other people are going on holiday and he will be left behind. Verbal explanations do not calm his distress and aggression.
>
> Alex is helped to understand by using an office calendar. The months are cut out and mounted on a dark background so that each month is a separate horizontal strip. It is easy to understand which way the days are being crossed off. A picture of a suitcase is placed on the date for his holiday. Now, even if he starts to get distressed when he hears someone say the word 'holiday', it is possible to negotiate with him: 'Look, we've got to here, there are all these days until your holiday.'
>
> We run our fingers along the days and point to the picture of the suitcase. We now have a way of negotiating with Alex which he can understand.

The backcloth to many people's lives is an unpredictable kaleidoscope of shifting changes and events. They do not know what will happen when or whom they will see today or, in fact, if they will ever see certain people again. It is not surprising that the people in the following histories are anxious.

Week

> **CAROLINE**, who has autism, constantly asks, 'Who is on today?'
>
> Caroline is reassured by a timetable which has hanging slats for each day to which photographs of support staff can be attached by velcro. The slats can be held in separate hands – a physical differentiation between one day and another or, even more crucially, *between 'now' and 'not now'*.

> **LIZ**, who has autism, is acutely anxious about going home at the weekend. This is reflected in her repetitive speech pattern: 'Monday, Tuesday, Wednesday, Thursday, Friday, Saturday, go home, see Mum' – which becomes increasingly distressed.
>
> *Continued...*

Liz is helped by a weekly timetable made of styrene panels, one for each day, held together by wide tape. The panels are set far enough apart to allow folding, so that any individual day can be isolated and discussed at any one time. Each day shows her activities. This catches her attention. Within a week Liz can say what she will do on any particular day. Although her speech is still within the 'sequence of days' stereotype, she has slowed down, her vocabulary has increased and she is less anxious.

Day

An ordinary timetable may be visually confusing if the person has no idea of left-to-right sequence. Flashcards on a board can be made with a dark reverse (see the picture below), so that when each event is finished, the card can be turned over, and there is a very clear visual distinction between what *has happened* and what is *going to happen*.

Another way to help understand what will happen in a day is to mount the works of a clock on a board with a white face and remove the minute hand. What is left is the hour hand as an indicator which points to appropriate velcro-attached pictures at the right time. This is very easy to do with modern electric clocks. The parts cost a few pounds and all that is needed is a board with the right size hole drilled in it. Because the hour-hand is short, it helps if a radial line is drawn from the picture to the circumference of the little-hand sweep.

Minutes

A kitchen timer can be helpful, particularly the wind-up kind which ticks and then pings when the time is reached. People who are worried about time can hear the tick and differentiate it from the ping. It gives the brain something to focus on until the ping sounds. Marking the unnumbered part with a felt pen (as shown in the drawing opposite) helps a person to set their own time, long or short. This gives them control.

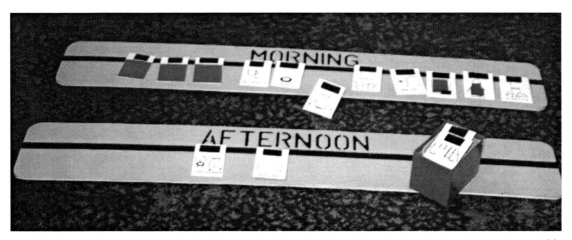

Day timetable

Waiting

Some people are extremely thirsty, they are fixated on drinks. Sometimes it helps to give smaller drinks more frequently but, if they cannot understand time, the question they ask themselves and us is, 'When am I going to get my next drink?'

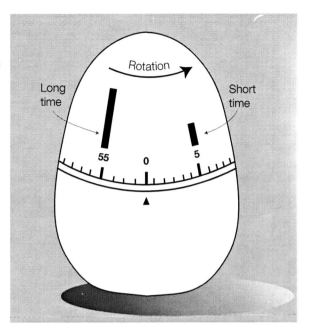

Kitchen timer

This becomes extremely stressful, especially so if the person has autistic tendencies. In a fragmenting world, teatime is a fixed point. ('I know what is happening and what I am doing when I am drinking my tea. I can relax.') As soon as teatime is past, tension starts to rise until the next teatime. 'When is it going to happen?' The brain asks this question over and over again. It may be an addiction to tea but it is compounded by not understanding time. 'Soon' or 'later' or even 'in five minutes' have no linear meaning, but hearing the tick of the timer ('not now') helps me to wait for the ping ('when I can have my tea'); it helps me to know where I am so that stress does not accumulate so easily.

We might also use the 'clock' described above, with a picture of 'their' teacup at the appropriate times.

It also helps to try to find an interesting occupation to fill in the gaps to divert the brain from its repetitive message. For example, with a more able person, one might build, hand-over-hand, shelves to hold their mugs and tea-caddy.

Sometimes a person with very severe learning disabilities may not be able to tolerate a long wait, even with the aids described above. Two hours can be broken down with the aid of a jar, eight wooden balls and a fifteen-minute eggtimer. Each time the timer pings, a ball is put in the jar. Attention is held by the tick and anticipation of the ping. Time is negotiated by the number of balls still not posted. If the person cannot count, even one ball left indicates that the two hours is not yet up – a concrete way of distinguishing between 'now' and 'not now'.

When behavioural difficulties relate to the absence of structure in people's lives, it is crucial that where behaviour improves as a consequence of introducing this structure, the structuring elements are not discontinued. This can happen easily: 'She's better now, I didn't think we needed to go on.'

This is a misunderstanding. It is the changes in a person's environment and not in personal behaviour which have brought about a reduction in reactive behaviour. The reduction does not mean that anxiety and confusion have gone away. They will reappear if the structure is withdrawn and the person is once more faced with unanticipated events. Consistency and continuity are vital.

Working with feelings

'Feeling' is a word with a wide range of meanings. It can be used in the sense of touch, emotion (what we feel), perception (what we sense others are feeling) and insight. For some people, their emotional lives have such dark undertows that they find it difficult to acknowledge them, and this link can lead to their rejection of the perceptual and empathetic aspects of our work. (In this respect, we should remember that although we may not be able to rationalise why we empathise with a particular course of action, we can measure outcomes.) We need to ask ourselves if the method we are using is working in a way which benefits the individual. This is the key question.

In practice, the dynamic of 'feeling' interactions is complex. There are our own feelings about ourselves, our work and the people with whom we are working. If we have not assimilated our own feelings, we may project these on to the people with whom we are working – as is common in many of our relationships. We need to be aware of this possibility.

However, there are times when we appear to be genuinely filled with an insight into, or an awareness of, how another person is feeling. Although it is difficult to understand how this occurs, it happens most frequently when we have come empty-handed to an encounter, perhaps sufficiently emptied of ourselves to pick up subliminal clues and attitudes which would normally be masked by our own agenda. This is illustrated by the next history:

I meet a woman I do not know and, telling her my name, ask what hers is. She hangs her head and says, 'I haven't got a name.'

My reaction to this is, for me, quite unexpected. Instead of trying to jolly her along (maternal instinct: trying to make things better – a process which would not have valued how she felt and therefore would not value her as an individual), I feel myself, quite literally, being sucked into an abyss of being so non-person that I haven't got a name. I hear myself say, 'Is that how it feels sometimes, not even having a name?'

She looks up at me and laughs: 'Yes, my name's Jane and you're a lovely lady.'

Naming her feeling releases a flood of cheerful conversation and interaction.

I find that, where it is possible to achieve it, an attitude of emptiness which is both alert (to all the activities and potential of the person) and detached (from my own agenda – particularly what I feel I, or the other person, 'ought' to be doing), is the most helpful position to adopt.

Very often when working with people with profound disabilities or complex challenging behaviour, it is only when I have exhausted my own resources – the preconceived ideas or equipment I have brought with me – even when I am turning away, in this void, that I begin to see the dynamic of what is going on and the person begins to respond. It is as though what I personally have to offer can actually block fluid interaction. The characteristic of these insights is that they are both surprising and fleeting. The moment needs to be grasped quickly, both for the person we are with, so that we can show them that we value them, and for ourselves, so that we can scrutinise the insight and evaluate it, beginning to unravel its implications. Evaluation against practice is one of the ways to distinguish between insight and projection.

It is at this level of feeling that my 'self' can truly share with another person. In terms of the locked room, this is where we can jointly open the window, lean out and enjoy the new view together. It is the moment when we say 'yes' to each other.

This therapeutic approach can lead to entanglements with a management system which demands benefit evaluations and asks: 'What will be the *outcome* of six weeks' intervention?'

Unfortunately, empowerment and growth do not lend themselves easily to cost analysis. One of the reasons we have actually been failing to get in touch with people who are locked in their own worlds is that our own agendas have masked the ways – in many cases, the ingenious ways – which people with severe disabilities have developed of understanding and relating to the realities they face.

After we had worked together with people who experienced great difficulties in their lives, a speech therapist said, 'I see that I have to put aside my language and learn theirs.'

We have to learn to put aside *everything* – preconceptions, philosophies, rules, 'occupations' – and focus on who the person is, aware of all they do and are, present for them so that nothing else matters.

Flexibility is the key to this way of working and outcomes can only be measured in retrospect.

All we can do is create optimum conditions which experience has taught us are likely to promote success. Whether the person will smile, laugh, relax and begin to relate are questions we cannot answer until we have tried.

Some of our experiences – and the emotions which stem from them – are too painful for us even to be aware of them. We forget or bury them in order to shield ourselves. Asking directly about them is counter-productive but sometimes we can bring about situations in which people feel safe enough to allow these feelings to emerge so that we can speak of them. One way of going about this is through the design and use of therapeutic games.

RON, a man with severe challenging behaviour, is unable to say why he attacks people. If asked, he becomes genuinely distressed and tearful.

Working on the premise that we all have different parts of us which act in conflicting ways, we design a board game with a format which resembles Monopoly. Each player has two pieces, a 'goody' and a 'baddy' who go round the board in opposite directions. (In order to make it clear that the game is not about being 'good' or 'bad', the characters are deliberately stereotypic – there must be no moral verdict on behaviour.) Each square is a situation with alternative outcomes – for example:

You are at the dentist and afraid. Do you:

a) tell him and ask him for an injection?

b) bite him?

If the 'goody' and the 'baddy' land on the same square, specially designed dice are used to decide the outcome. The aim of the game – where both players have an equal chance of the 'baddy' coming out on top – is to stimulate conversation, laughter and being with each other in a way that feels safe and accepting enough to talk about how we feel. It is all right and normal to feel angry, unhappy and frustrated. We all do.

We play for several months. One day Ron says, 'You know, I'm not going to get better while I feel so angry.'

This is a breakthrough for him. Although the situation is still complex, he is able to start caring for his parents who have become disabled.

This is a man who is totally unable to understand or communicate why he feels impelled to attack people. Ron cannot feel his anger – it is unknown to him – but he is periodically overcome by situations that he sees as life-threatening, so he responds accordingly. He describes it as 'a black cloud moving up through him' – more of a physical description than an emotion. It does not appear to be related to epilepsy.

Some people appear to try to protect themselves from others coming too close to them by using repetitive speech patterns.

CAROL, a woman who seems closed off from others, uses a very tight pattern of three sentences about a famous personality. Trying to ignore this or override it results in her becoming increasingly agitated.

We decide to use a poster of 'her personality' to work with Carol. We place the poster between a transparent plastic sheet and a white backboard. Using a large felt pen, we draw round the head and remove the photograph, leaving the outline. I suggest she adds more hair. Carol picks up the pen and adds some. In subsequent sessions, she starts to talk more about the personality. After another two sessions, she suddenly becomes extremely angry. She expresses this by scribbling very hard on her picture and telling us how she feels about her life. After this incident, Carol is able to talk more freely about normal things such as wanting to go shopping.

Some more-able people are able to express themselves and talk about their feelings through a keyboard when they cannot do so through speech. An indirect approach is essential: use of the third person and statements rather than questions are less threatening. It may be possible to contain and hold feelings in the computer which otherwise feel dangerous and overwhelming.

It is not only extremely important that we try to create a space in which people feel safe enough to express their feelings but that, when they do, we really *listen* to what they are trying to tell us. When I told staff that the woman had hung her head and said she had no name, they said she always did that. But Jane was not trying to say that she had literally never been given a name; rather, she was trying to tell us what it feels like to be so under-valued and powerless that she does not feel she qualifies as an individual. The anger of Ron, with whom I played the game 'goodies and baddies' is so powerful that if he allows himself to feel it as an emotion, he fears it will destroy him. For whatever reason, Carol, who talks about the well-known personality, feels so vulnerable that she cannot bear meaningful interactions with other people.

Individuals who are living in these types of situations are experiencing stress. Sometimes they are able to devise coping strategies to protect themselves but more often the pressures build up into outbursts which are either self-destructive or aggressive, situations which we experience as 'challenging behaviour'. The challenge for us is to look for ways in which we can ease their tension. We have to try to examine all aspects of their lives from their point of view: how does their life feel to them? This is the subject of the next history, which is about a man who was very disturbed indeed.

Precious objects

JIM, who has severe learning disabilities and challenging behaviour, is admitted to hospital when his parents can no longer manage. He breaks up furniture on a daily basis and eats plastic. He is unable to relate to people in any positive way and is heavily sedated to the point where he is unsteady on his feet and often falls. He does not speak meaningfully.

In a new ward, the team leader and I take a look at the cycle of Jim's behaviour. He breaks furniture to obtain plastic bits which he then eats, as they are otherwise taken away. As he no longer has his plastic, he breaks up more furniture looking for replacements.

I take Jim to my workshop and, using power tools with hand-on-hand prompt, together we make a box for him to keep his bits in. He understands its purpose perfectly and keeps it by his bed. He stops needing new bits and therefore stops breaking furniture. X-rays show that the number of pieces of plastic in his stomach is reduced from thirty-five before the intervention to one a month later. Because his behaviour improves, Jim's medication is reduced. He can now walk and run. His motivation is improved and he can now make his needs understood using speech. With his key-worker, Jim now goes to evening classes in woodwork and, when we meet, he shows me with great pride a construction he has made.

Trying to keep objects that are precious to a person may lead to their walking around with them or even eating them. It is not only that they feel the need to keep the objects safe but sometimes they feel as if their own safety depends on the presence of their particular things.

Jim's bits of plastic are extremely precious to him. In spite of all the trouble they bring him, his need to keep them is overridingly powerful, almost like our early need for transitional objects when, as children, we cling to the safety of a loved blanket, which is our half-way house to independence. We resist vigorously any attempt to remove it. Taking it away is equivalent to separation from a parent. Jim's need is that strong. In order to give him confidence, we need to find a way of helping him to protect his things instead of taking them away. Again, this shows that we value what he values and by implication, that we value him.

This technique of making boxes to hold what a person values has been used with a number of disturbed people. It can be extended to making (together) shelves to hold people's precious objects. Doing it together is crucial. Even if the person is only able to pass the screws, they are taking part, it is theirs. The outcome has always been beneficial. Once a person knows that their objects are safely contained and that they can control them, their need for them usually diminishes and they can move on to other activities.

Nurturing

Not everyone can speak. One of the roots of distress which seems to affect some women is the lack of opportunity to give birth and bring up babies. These women often respond very positively to life-size images of babies, enlarged photocopies mounted on plywood (as shown in the picture below).

CATHERINE sits in her chair and hits anyone who comes near.

I show Catherine images of babies and she puts out her hands and says, 'ahhh.' She becomes creative in her 'play' with the 'baby', putting it behind a mirror with a hole in it so that just the eye shows. She laughs at it. Her key-worker works hard using it with her. Not only is she interested and involved with the images but over the next three weeks she learns to greet visitors with a hug instead of hitting them. This instinctive empathy response is hormonal. It appears that repeated experience of the empathy response has changed the way Catherine was able to relate to people.

We have learned to pay attention to the sexual needs of the people with whom we work but little, if any, to their need to nurture. We know that the absence of opportunity to give birth and raise children can cause great pain. In spite of this, it is not generally a factor which is taken into account in the lives of women with severe learning disabilities. It is absolutely essential that we learn to show that we respect these feelings, to make it clear that they are meaningful to us. At the same time, we have to be careful not to raise expectations which cannot be fulfilled and for this reason I find it preferable to work with representations rather than dolls – pictures seem to be enough to introduce the idea and work with the feelings without inspiring hopes that cannot be met.

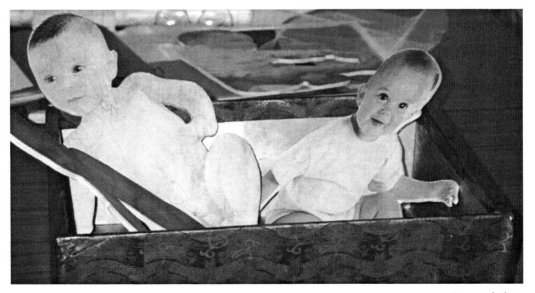

Picture babies

Chapter Seven

EMPOWERMENT AND RESPECT

How do we help people to feel good about themselves when, even if they have received loving care, their perception of what it means to be a human being is of living in an environment which is at best puzzling, but may be very frightening indeed, and one in which they have no effective control?

Before we can answer this question, we have to put ourselves in their place and look at their situation from their unique point of view. We find ourselves in a world that is, for one reason or another, stressful. We are unable to let people know what we need and we are, to a large extent, dependent upon the basic signals afforded by body language.

A dual approach

Looking from inside outwards enables us to see that we, as supporters, need to adopt a combined approach of **stress reduction** and **confidence building**, considering both the outer (environmental) and inner (personal) elements which affect an individual's life. We should address those things in a person's life which increase tension as well as working through people's personal language to refocus their attention on an outside world which they can experience as friendly, welcoming, interesting and supportive.

Stress reduction

Stress reduction is often accomplished by paying respectful attention to some aspect of a person's life which may seem very minor to us but is extremely important to them. The following list of areas to which we should be paying attention does not include the issues of loss and bereavement or the anger that some people may express, if they are able, towards their disabilities and sometimes towards the non-disabled world in which they live. How does lack of ability feel in a world based on competence?

Hypersensitivities

As we have seen, a person's experience of sound, or being looked at or spoken to directly, may be different to ours and even painful. We may be able to address their needs by speaking softly or by indirect communication.

Non-confrontational body language

We need to remember the difficulties that a person may experience with boundaries and use non-confrontational body language. This involves the realisation that some of our gestures and behaviours, which are unintentional or even well-intentioned, may be perceived as frightening or even painful. We need to think about how our movements and positions and proximity appear to others; a person who stands over them or too near them or even, in some cases, looks directly at them, may be seen as intimidating and the person responds as though they are under threat – by withdrawal or attack. If it is difficult for a person to hold together a stationary image, how much more difficult is a world and people which move?

Valuing feelings

Every opportunity should be taken to help people express how they feel and to be sensitive to their feelings. We need to value people and also show that we value what they value devising, if necessary, ways of helping them to contain their precious objects. We need to be sensitive to the deprivation which may arise from their lack of opportunity to nurture and raise children.

Negotiation and control

We need to develop the skill of negotiation so that we can help people increase control over the conflicts that really affect them – those concerned with relationship, their inner lives and the tensions which arise out of expectations based on realities different from their own. For example, it is hard to relate to people if they appear as fragments, and you do not know what they want.

Structure

If people do not know what is going to happen when and have no sense of order, time, interval or sequence, we need to help them by introducing timetables, timers, visual aids and objects of reference which are specifically designed for that individual so that they can be understood. If the person cannot understand these, we can sometimes still help by being present for the person in a way that respects their difficulties.

One support worker who has particular sensitivity to the person with whom she works says that when this person is feeling bad she sits in the next room with the door open. She can then be seen but is not invasive.

We must try to make it possible for people always to be able to know what is going to happen when and the difference between 'now' and 'not now'.

Environment

We need to remember that certain people are unable to cope with environments which are small and noisy. They may find other people intolerable. All these factors contribute to stress. Peeters points out that some people may also not be equipped to cope with the ideal of community living:

> 'Although social interaction is difficult for people with autism, the accent
> in group homes is put on group experience and group activities.'[16]

For example, we may expect that all residents will go swimming, although the pool may be echoing and noisy for an individual who is hypersensitive to sound.

Building confidence

At the same time as trying to reduce stress levels, we need to work on building confidence through getting in touch by improving relationships. This book has addressed in detail the possibilities of Intensive Interaction (using a person's own language) and interactive activities (activities with which an individual can connect). We also need to pay particular attention to valuing what the person values and finding ways to hand over control. We need to try to help people build an internal picture of themselves as having individual lives.

This can be done with photographs (enlarged on a photocopier to A4 size) of all aspects of their lives and activities which can be presented in plastic display books. It is important that these are not just portraits but pictures of the individual 'doing' things in order to encourage conversation about them and their lives, to recall the good times and give opportunities to explore the sadder times. We need something to talk to each other about. Audio and video tapes help revisit an experience and reinforce the person's part in and relation to it.

An equal partnership?

In his contribution to the book *Making Connections*, Robinson says:

> 'Fundamentally, we need to develop a philosophy which provides a sound basis
> for valuing and respecting all human beings, including those with learning
> disabilities, regardless of their capabilities, performance or appearance.'[17]

I am sure that most of us would concur with this. If this is so, why, in spite of our best intentions and positive mission statements, is it not happening for some of the people with whom we work?

Perhaps the first thing we need to look at very carefully is: what are the underlying implications of saying that we respect and value a person?

The rationale is that each person is unique. While some of us come wrapped in better packaging than others, what we all have in common is our humanity.

Sometimes humanity can be hidden behind disabilities and challenging behaviour, however. We feel cut off from the person. We get no feedback, or negative feedback, from them. When this happens, it is easy to allow more immediate feelings to determine the way we relate to the person.

> **MICK** crouches in the corner of the room. If approached, he gets up, rushes through the centre, hits anyone he comes across and then returns to a corner. Support staff have tried every way of getting his attention – he will not focus on anything.
>
> I stand away from Mick so as not to disturb him and look at him very carefully. He is, in fact, concentrating very hard on one particular activity – digging his fingernails into the palm of his closed fist. It is not easy to spot: all you can see is the tendons moving on the back of his hand.
>
> I hold my hand up in the air so that he can see it and reflect his movements back to him. It takes about twenty minutes before he notices. Once he sees what I am doing, he begins to attend to me and focus on the movements of my fingers. I stop. He waits to see if I will start again. We start to alternate. I gradually bring down my hand and walk across to him, continuing with our 'conversation'. When I am near, he lets me place my hand on his and join in his movements. He starts to smile. Within ten minutes we are 'playing' all sorts of hand games which he initiates. We are laughing together and feel a bond between us.

If I had been asked, before I started to work with him, whether I valued and respected this man as an equal, rationally I should have said, 'yes'; but if I had been totally honest, then I should have admitted that my overriding connection with Mick at this time was the feeling that I was afraid of him. He behaved like a wild man. His humanity was obscured for me by his behaviour. It was difficult to stand back and view him other than through the spectacles of my own timidity. Once we were engaged with each other in a shared activity which we both enjoyed, the perspective shifted. We were two people who were present for each other in every sense of the word.

More subtle than our immediate responses are the blueprints which we all carry with us: for example, the ways we related to our parents; our need to control; or, for some, the need to 'mother' with all that this implies. These are the walls we place round ourselves and they obscure for us who the other person actually is.

The mother of a woman with severe epilepsy and autism said that until she had learned to work interactively with her daughter, she felt that she had only been able to relate to her as a child who needed to be looked after, **but now she could relate to her as a person and talk to her all the time**.

When we work interactively, we work from inner person to inner person in the context of total respect for who the other person is, not who we feel they ought to be. Far from treating people as children, we are enhancing their dignity as individuals. We are taking part in a process that transcends disability and age.

> **MEHMET**, who has severe cerebral palsy, has the use of one hand.
>
> Mehmet learns to use a sewing machine handle and together we make cushions and a quilt for his bedroom. He is very pleased with these. One day when I come in, he leans across and with great difficulty manages to grab a cushion and pass it to me. I say, 'Yes, we made that together, didn't we?'
>
> But it is not the acknowledgement that he wants. Mehmet wants me to be comfortable. It is something he can do for me. I realise that in all the years I have been working with Mehmet, I have been so focused on my own contribution to our partnership that I have not allowed him room to be himself, to feel about me as I do about him. I have not valued his feelings as a man.

In order to relate to people, we need to empty ourselves of our own programmes and become vulnerable, so that we can learn from the other person as well as they from us. This is the equality that allows us to respect a person for who they are. We need to be able to enter their world on their terms so that they can relate without being afraid. As Williams says of a relationship, describing a photograph of herself and her partner:

"This is me in 'my world' and him in 'my world', not always having to struggle to be in 'their world'."[12]

This is respect, the respect which values another person enough to give them space to be their true selves, not 'respectability' with which it is so often confused. Respectability seeks to conform a person to 'our world' without giving value to their worth as an individual. While image is important in that it has a bearing on how a person is perceived and treated by our world, equally important is how a person is able to view themselves. Being socially acceptable is not enough if, at the same time, a person feels isolated, a prisoner in their own world. We need to learn to share our enjoyment and pleasure in each other's company so that people can grow in confidence and begin to reach out, on their terms, to a world beyond the private place in which they have been locked. This is how we can empower people and give them confidence. This is a beginning, the freeing-up of potential.

We need to ask ourselves if the interactions we are having with a person are enriching their lives. Does what we are doing enable them to be closer to their true selves and live more freely and confidently, at whatever level?

Finally, whatever our theoretical standpoint, is what we are doing *working* for this person? If we cannot answer 'yes', we need to re-examine our premises.

We must be able to answer: 'yes'.

Appendix

TRAINING

by Pene Stevens

All over the country, services are having difficulty getting in touch with a small but significant proportion of clients who are not able to respond to the services which are provided for them.

Enough work has been done in this field to show that use of the techniques discussed in this book is an extremely effective way of empowering many of these people and transforming their lives. It usually costs very little but, because the work is relatively new and sometimes introduces premises that do not always sit comfortably with other approaches which have been tried, it requires thought and training.

If it is to be successful, the approach must be understood by senior management and incorporated into the structure of individual houses. Because it requires frequent interventions and embraces all aspects of people's lives, the only practical way that this work can be carried out is by unqualified staff, supervised and supported by senior qualified staff and therapists who are familiar with the techniques.

Obviously, all the people involved are going to require training at the appropriate level. Experience suggests that this training is best done *in situ*, working with the people with whom the support teams are having difficulty. Staff are far more likely to be convinced and given the confidence to try these techniques themselves if they have seen them work with people they already know.

Training presents enormous problems. One is the very high turnover of staff. Another was highlighted recently by a training officer who commented that in a group of eighteen unqualified staff who came recently for training, three were unable to read or write. In another group was an individual who spoke no English at all. In the same groups, there may well be graduates. The range is extensive.

On top of difficulties with understanding, there is the equally important question of emotional sensitivity. What are the qualities we are looking for? We may need to employ people on the grounds of availability who, in their own lives, have never had the security which enables them to abandon the more traditional position of control. In addition, they are almost certainly not familiar with the practice of being able to stand back and assess their own attitudes and interventions.

Against this background, how do we go about setting up an interactive approach in a group home, the aims of which will include reducing stress so that residents feel secure and building up their confidence?

Setting up such an interactive approach breaks down into three main areas:

1 how do we train staff?

2 how do we put training into practice?

3 how do we ensure that this style of practice is maintained?

1 How do we train staff?

Training needs to be experiential to enable staff to feel what it might be like to be the person with whom they are working. Role play and active exercises encourage relevant reflection and insight . For example, many people with severe learning disabilities have some degree of visual or hearing loss. Exercises using blindfolds or earmuffs which mirror these disabilities help staff to understand more clearly the kind of support people need – a person with visual loss finds it easier if they know where other people are in relation to them.

How does this apply to Ella, a woman with severe tunnel vision, who spends much of her time wandering round the fairly busy hallway? The 'blindfold' exercises highlight for staff the difficulties Ella faces in understanding what is going on round her. Feedback from this exercise includes remarks such as:

● 'it was frightening.'

● 'I couldn't work out where I was although I knew the layout.'

This enables staff to understand why it is important actually to tell Ella where they are and what they are doing: 'I am just coming past you to go and turn off the washing machine.'

A light touch values Ella as a person and includes her in the activities which are going on in her house. She knows what is happening.

Sometimes, however, Ella is jostled by other residents and becomes confused and upset, throwing herself to the floor, screaming. Now it is staff who need to know what is happening. To help them understand, another training technique uses brief case studies describing similar situations and invites staff to reflect on why the person might be behaving in such a way and what would be the most helpful response.

In Ella's particular case staff need to:

- recognise she is upset and why

- empathise with that feeling instead of trying to jolly her along

- take action to show their support, that is, lie on the floor beside her until she is calm and ready to get up instead of trying to get Ella to her feet while she is still upset. Support staff are often surprised to find that this approach works.

This experiential training enables staff to move from their instinctive reaction to pull Ella up, to the perceptive response of reflecting back her state of mind in a way that values her, a response which has a successful outcome. The staff are working with Ella rather than against her.

This formal training needs to be set alongside and reinforced by in-house demonstration of techniques. It can be greatly helped by periodic evaluation of videotaped activities.

2 How do we put training into practice?

Training which helps staff to understand the best ways of supporting people, reducing stress and helping them to feel secure, needs to go hand in hand with techniques for building up their confidence such as Intensive Interaction and interactive activities.

Ella responds to rhythms of music she hears. Picking this up, staff focus with her on drumming, at which she becomes very proficient. She begins to smile and laugh out loud in a way she rarely has before. Through watching video recordings, staff notice that Ella's posture changes from being hunched up to an upright position, and her gestures become more open and expansive. At the same time, since she is getting more one-to-one interaction, and therefore staff are talking to her more frequently to explain what is happening, Ella's speech and vocabulary improve. Staff can see that she is becoming more confident.

Underlying all these approaches is the importance of teaching staff careful and accurate observation skills. House leaders need to take the lead, spending time with residents, pointing out to staff what they see and initiating discussion. Staff need to know that their observations will be valued and considered by house leaders. Time must be set aside for staff to practise such skills. More importantly, staff need to feel that observation and 'being with people' is a part of their role. Domestic chores, while they may provide an important source of interaction, should not be allowed to assume dominance, as they so often do.

3 How do we ensure that this style of practice is maintained?

Given that the house leader is aware, in the ways discussed above, of the needs of their residents, what are the factors which result in effective implementation of the approach in one house but not in another? For example, most homes have individual care plans but they are not always carried out.

The structure needs to be clear. In the author's service, which consists of homes for people with severe and profound disabilities and extra support needs, small key-teams have been developed around each person, consisting of a leader (in this case a qualified nurse) supporting and supervising two support workers who key-work an individual. These teams meet regularly, with each member of staff having an individual supervision session every month between meetings. Every six months, all staff take part in a study day.

Staff need to be clear what is expected of them. House leaders need to emphasise that the main work centres around the individual and their care plan. Significant interactions must be recorded on daily checklists. Staff need to know that their work is going to be examined in depth, both in supervision – where the emphasis will be on their skills, thoughts and feelings about their key-resident – and in client care meetings – where the emphasis is more on the resident.

While the key-worker is responsible for an individual, the team will be involved when the key-worker is away. The key-worker is accountable for the carrying out of the care plan and so exerts peer pressure on any team member who is not performing to standard.

The quality of the care plan is vital. Records need to be carefully designed so that staff see the need for keeping them. They must know that relevant information will be used: it will be evaluated and used as the basis for updating care plans at client care meetings. House leaders must check every aspect of the care plan. New needs and relationships will be supported.

So what makes one house effective and another not? It is evident that clear and informed leadership is crucial with high expectations and good communication. The more that people understand what is expected of them, the less need there is to chase them on an individual basis.

The benefit of this style of working is a more interactive team with increased motivation which focuses on enabling rather than caring and on empowering rather than controlling. The emphasis is on the resident and, as their skills increase, there is more job satisfaction and therefore lower staff turnover. The purpose of the paperwork in such a process is clearly seen and understood by all staff.

In order to train sufficient people, including where necessary introducing the relevant techniques to house leaders, it would help in large service areas to employ one or more practice development officers, whose duties would include visiting each of a group of homes or residential units once every week to pick up exactly what is going on. In this way they could highlight the needs of individual service users, picking up on particular difficulties; for example, how is it best to work with a man who is hypersensitive to sound? Practice development officers would then come back with video analyses and role play, spending time with individual support staff and helping the whole team to develop better and more effective ways of communication and interaction.

While practice development officers would need to include shift work in their remit, so that they can reach the whole team, they should not be regarded as an extra pair of hands. Their role should be to stand back, observe and train. In order to attract the right calibre candidate and so that such training is seen as fundamental to practice by management, the practice development officer would need to be employed at the level of an H-grade nurse, depending on their profession. This would ensure that a nurse, for example, could be research-based. A person would not have to leave clinical practice in order to pursue their career.

While this may seem impractical for small agencies, it is important to remember that the approaches outlined above can be cost-effective, as well as transforming the lives of people who have, until now, been seen as beyond the reach of our skills. However the service is delivered, to be effectively embedded it must be seen as being valued by management.

REFERENCES

1 Caldwell, P. A. (1996) *Getting In Touch*. Brighton: Pavilion Publishing/Joseph Rowntree Foundation.

2 Ephraim, G. W. (1986) *A Brief Introduction to Augmented Mothering*. Playtrack Pamphlet, Harperbury Hospital, Radlett, Herts.

3 Nind, M. & Hewett, D. (1994) *Access to Communication*. David Fulton Press.

4 Hewett, D. & Nind, M. (1998) *Interaction in Action*. David Fulton Press.

5 Williams, D. (1992) *Nobody Nowhere*. London: Doubleday.

6 Stern, D. (1985) *The Interpersonal World of the Infant*. London: Basic Books, Harper Collins.

7 Ephraim, G. Personal communication.

8 Williams, D. (1996) *Autism: An Inside-Out Approach*. London: Jessica Kingsley.

9 Barron, J. & Barron, S. (1992) *There's a Boy in Here*. New York: Simon and Schuster.

10 Jolliffe, T., Lansdown, R. & Robinson, C. (1992) Autism: A personal account. *Communication*, **26** (3).

11 Dunbar R. (1996) *Grooming, Gossip and the Evolution of Language*. Faber and Faber.

12 Williams, D. *Jam-Jar*. Channel 4 Film.

13 Birath, G. Personal communication.

14 Howlin, P. (1997) *Autism: Preparing for Adulthood*. London: Routledge.

15 Weekes, L. *A Bridge of Voices*. Radio Four.

16 Peeters, T. (1997) *Autism: From Theoretical Understanding to Educational Intervention*. Whyrr Publishers Ltd.

17 Robinson, T. (1989) *Making Connections. Reflecting on the Lives of People with Learning Disabilities*. Brechin, A. & Walmsley, J. (Eds.) London: Hodder and Stoughton.

AVAILABLE FROM
PAVILION PUBLISHING:

Getting In Touch

Also by Phoebe Caldwell:

Published by Pavilion Publishing in association with The Joseph Rowntree Foundation
The author's first book describing her techniques for responding to the individual needs
of people with severe learning disabilities and extensive support needs through careful
observation and familiar stimuli.

Format: A4 manual, *42pp*

The Susie Brown Intervention Maze

John Shephard

Published by Pavilion Publishing in association with Hastings and Rother NHS Trust
Experience the dilemmas, frustrations and successes of behavioural intervention within
a hypothetical scenario. Susie Brown is a fictional service user who presents challenges
to her staff group. As a member of Susie's staff group you must decide what action to take
in order to plan an effective response to her difficulties.

Format: Ring bound option sheets (*60pp*) and trainer's notes (*85pp*)

Approaches to People with Challenging Behaviour

Published by the University of St Andrews

A training and distance learning package for direct care staff working with people
with challenging behaviour. Winner of the British Partnership Award for Innovation
in Open Learning.

Format: Large ring binder containing student notes, activities, practitioner notes
and certification option.

Approaches to People with Profound and Complex Disabilities

Published by the University of St Andrews
in association with Fife Regional Council
Endorsed by Enable

This attractively produced open learning package is designed to enhance skills in direct
care staff working with clients with profound and complex disabilities.

Format: Large ring binder containing portfolio exercises, group activities, background
information and references to further reading (*350pp*).